Mel Bay Presents

MARK O'CONNOR CONTEST FIDDLING

by Stacy Phillips

ACKNOWLEDGEMENTS

I would like to thank these folks for the generous help they offered to ease the assemblage of this book:
Richard Blaustein
Earl Spielman
Brooks Otis of Wildwood Music – Arcata, California
Rich Levine
Phil and Vivian Williams of Voyager Records
Dave Freeman of Country Records
Bill Harrison of The Devil's Box magazine
Russ Barenberg
Marty O'Connor
Pam Swing of the University of Texas

I am also grateful to Benny Thomasson and Mark O'Connor for granting interviews.

Finally to all the fiddlers named in this book, thanks for the great music. This book is dedicated to them.

Visit us on the Web at www.melbay.com — E-mail us at email@melbay.com

CONTENTS

INTRODUCTION

"Saturday noon in northwest Connecticut. It is a small town's Banjo, Guitar, Band and Fiddle Contest on The Green. If I am going to write about it I might as well experience it, so I decide to enter my first fiddle competition.

Within minutes of arrival I am requisitioned to back up a singing appearance by Miss Connecticut, a bizarre and inauspicious beginning.

The top prizes in the old-timey and open categories are fifty dollars, so most of the entrants are within an hour's drive. Still there is a high level of ability with New England, Texas, Irish and Southeastern styles all represented.

Contestants accompany each other on stage. I reacquaint myself with old picking friends and meet a few new ones. All are fine players. No chance for me to place. It does not matter. Love of playing some old tunes (and lust for easy money) join us together. The potpourri of simultaneously practiced tunes is a beautiful bedlam.

Who won the Open? Oh no! Bah! My first taste of contest injustice. Still, the main reason for the contest is successfully accomplished — the locals have a chance to dust off their instruments, and some fine music is made on a summer day. It is not a total loss anyway. I play Dobro with an ad hoc band that comes in second. I win some cash. I am hooked. Now I can write about the contest scene with authority."

Fiddle contests have sprouted like mushrooms in the past few years. This reflects a general growth of interest in non-classical violin and has been accompanied by the spread of a style that is particularly attractive to younger players and suited to the contest milieu. This manner of fiddling originated in Texas but is now on its way towards becoming a national style. It is great to listen to and play and it can serve as a fruitful training ground for launching into bluegrass and swing.

This book is not an attempt at a scholarly analysis of the Texas style though I try to point out some of its salient characteristics. My music sources are contests, records and jam sessions. I have listened to several renditions of the tunes, then picked out my favorite variations of each to give an idea of the art of altering a fiddle tune and a feel for the wide range of Texas fiddling.

This is the first book to present fiddle tunes in the way they are actually played, with all the variations and ornamentations of the best players of the style.

Some of these tunes have not yet become the object of extensive reworking but by the time you get through this music you should be able to authentically vary them on your own.

This music is best transmitted aurally not by music notation. Listen to some of the records in the discography. Use the accompanying cassette tape to become familiar with the tunes. Then start picking it out on your fiddle. When you get bogged down use the written music. Such exercise educates your musical ear, an important attribute for any musician. Even though it seems easier to just read the music, the lesson is best learned when learned by ear.

In the introductions to each tune I have listed the fiddlers I have used as references for the arrangements that follow, but any of the players mentioned in this book (and others as well) could have been cited. This music is the collective improvisation of hundreds of fiddlers over many years.

If you are not comfortable with the caprices of music notation, take it slowly. Leave out the ornamentations (slurs, grace notes and triplets) until you can chug along at a slow speed. Remember though that the tunes are arranged to be played close to the indicated tempos. Changing them may call for altered bowing.

Play the chords through to become attuned to the harmonic background. The streams of notes will then make more sense.

With all the great sounding variations that follow and the competitive feeling that makes you enter a contest, do not lose sight of what the whole scene is about - celebrating the music that comes out of your fiddle. These motifs and licks have been reworked and honed by generations of musicians. The most successful experiments are absorbed into the fiddle community. The products are masterpieces of fiddle music. Enjoy and learn.

EXPLANATION OF SYMBOLS

means a slide of indeterminate length (most always short) up to the indicated note.

means an indeterminate slide downwards from the indicated note.

means a slide of exact length between the indicated notes.

all notes enclosed by a slur sign are played with one bow stroke.

"PIZZ" means to pluck the string with a finger of your bowing hand.

"ARCO" means to return to bowing.

"MM" refers to the standard metronome markings.

Numbers in parentheses above the leger lines are recommended fingerings.

THE TEXAS FIDDLING STYLE

Old time fiddling was already going out of style when it reached North America from The British Isles and France. In the eighteenth century these countries were not as influenced by 'art music' as the rest of Europe. Bow strokes were short, open string drones were employed and vibrato was used sparingly. In addition the bow was held well above the frog and the instrument was often held against the player's chest. Above all, the violin played dance music.

By the time the invention of the phonograph record allowed the acoustical 'freezing' of a performance, this dance music had spawned at least four distinct styles, New England, Cajun, Southeastern, and Texas. The Southeast and Texas had many similarities (single shuffle bowing and cross tunings, for example) but the release of Alexander "Eck" Robertson's version of "Sally Goodin" in 1922 demonstrated that at least some Texans liked to modify and extend their tunes much more than their counterparts in other parts of the country. Robertson's version is a classic, taking the two part Southeast tune and adding about twelve variations, some quite musically removed from the original melody.

This way of working over tunes to avoid repetition was, and is spurred by the thriving contest tradition in Texas. Men like Robertson, Red Steeley, Ervin Solomon, Lefty Franklin, Oscar Harper, Major Franklin and Benny Thomasson have raised this tendency into a fine art of controlled improvisation. Of all these it is generally agreed that Benny Thomasson has done the most in creating and disseminating the modern Texas-based style that wins such major contests as Weiser, Idaho's National Old Time Fiddlers' Contest, Crockett, Texas' World Championships and Nashville, Tennessee's Grand Masters', as well as a majority of the smaller ones.

There are elements of old timey (ie. Southeastern sounding) and Western swing (by way of the area bands that featured fiddle, like Bob Wills and Milton Brown) in Texas fiddling, with the former giving it a traditional base and the latter some of its melodic inventiveness and harmonic accompaniment. This accompaniment features 'sock' or closed chording on the guitar. The strum is in swing style and many passing or implied chords are used, such as ninths and diminisheds.

What exactly makes contest fiddling a recognizable style cannot be completely described by words but here are some of the characteristics you can pick out as you go through the music.

The tempos of both hoedowns and waltzes are noticeably slower than in the Southeast. This allows concentration on more intricate and smooth bowing, and the technical aspects of playing in general.

Most of the bowing is one note per stroke but the change of direction is done very smoothly so the sound is not choppy. This makes exact decipherment of the bow pattern nearly impossible in hoedowns, but the indicated notations are quite close so do not stray too far.°Often the fiddler changes his pattern when repeating the same riff in one rendition. The choice of bowing is a big part of the rhythmic feel so experiment carefully. An incorrect mix of single bows and slurs can destroy the fiddle flavor of a tune.

Many Texas fiddlers hold the bow with their thumbs under the frog. Benny Thomasson says it helps him play with a loose wrist. The exceedingly loose bowing wrist helps smooth a change of bow direction. Compared to the Southeast the amount of bow used on each stroke is longer. Texans also use less bow pressure, especially compared to bluegrassers.

A pattern of two notes per stroke is often used, with the single shuffle being the most often used (although not nearly as much as in the Southeast). A single suffle is the following pattern, x x x x (in cut time it is represented by x x x x). It imparts an accent to the third note of four in the phrase. Texas fiddlers use this sparingly, and arrange the bowing to fit the note patterns they have chosen.

The bow rarely leaves the strings. You will find very few rests in the hoedowns. Benny Thomasson and Major Franklin occasionally throw a short one in for rhythmic spice. A few times per tune four to six notes will be played on one bow stroke. Triplets are almost always slurred. The steady stream of notes is interrupted at times by a prolonged double stop, usually at the beginning of a phrase.

°However, listen to the comments by the fiddlers on the "Contest Fiddling" cassette.

Very little dynamics are employed, especially on the up tempo numbers.

Benny Thomasson apparently increased the use of the third position. One of the stamps of the Texas style is the use of an upper hand position for several measures at a time, even a whole section. Other American fiddle styles might call for a jump to another position for just a few notes.

The employment of hemiolas as a syncopating device was borrowed from ragtime and swing. This is pattern of three notes, repeated in such a way as to have the same notes fall on different parts of the beat each time. For example check "Billy in the Lowground", measure 51, "Don't Let Your Deal Go Down", measures 82 to 85 and "Beaumont Rag", measures 33 to 40.

The Texas eighth note pattern is more swingy than other North American styles. It is played as [tied triplet, 3] (sometimes notated as [quarter-eighth triplet, 3]) as opposed to [two eighth notes]. To cut down on congestion in the music notation this 'tied triplet' feel is written as regular eighth notes. If you play them as written however, the music will come out too square.

In waltzes there is more concentration on tone. Double stops and slides are frequently employed and only a small amount of vibrato is permissible. These devices, combined with the slow tempos make in-tuneness critical.

With innovation encouraged, Texas contest tunes have many strains added to the basic melody. Some catch on and become part of the standard arrangement. These, in turn, are worked on and may bear other standard sections.

Most of the fiddlers arrange their pieces completely beforehand, but some like Benny Thomasson and Mark O'Connor are especially known for their improvising. They have the general outline of the order of variations established (eg. low part, then third position motif, then a strain beginning with a sustained double stop etc.) but within each segment they play around with the melody and rhythm.

With all these musical transformations and contrasts, the basic feeling of the old tunes is still present. Losing even radar contact with this results in losing points in the judging.

As one researcher (Linda Burman-Hall in Ethnomusicology, volume 19 (1975), page 47) puts it pedantically, Texas fiddling is characterized by

> "one measure rhythmic ostinati...with bowed duplets, trochaic triplets and sometimes iambic triplet subdivisions of beat. Fingering rhythms within bowing strokes avoid triplet subdivisions in favor of even duplets, presenting triplet subdivisions with all three pulses only as ornamentation."

Major Franklin sure would have been surprised to know that.

Stacy Phillips (Photo by Sarah Heath)

THE CONTEST TRADITION

Though there are surely more fiddle contests now than ever, they have been part of the American scene since before Independance. The earliest on record was in 1736. In November of that year, in the Virginia Colony, a horse race was held that featured as a sidelight, a playoff between twenty fiddlers for a ''Cremona fiddle".

> "As this Mirth is design'd to be purely innocent, and void of Offense, all Persons resorting there are desir'd to behave themselves with Decency and Sobriety; the Subscribers being resolv'd to discountenance all Immorality with the utmost Rigour."
>
> (quoted by Richard Hulan in The Devil's Box of March, 1969)

I am reasonably certain that the "Subscribers" had as little success controlling fiddlers in 1736 as promoters do now.

References to competitions are few before the late 19th century when a series of matches were begun in Atlanta, Georgia. Still, the occasional mention makes it clear that where there was a living fiddle tradition, there were contests. For example a two man clash is described by Andy Adams (in The Devil's Box of December, 1976). It takes place in Ogalalla in the Dakota Territory in 1882. The scene is a cow town and several herds have just paid off their hands. After the obligatory horse race two outfits challenge for the bragging rights to best fiddler.

> "The conditions governing the contest were given us, and two chuck wagons were drawn alongside each other, in one were seated the contestants and in the other the judges... Each fiddler selected his own piece. The first tune was a waltz, on the conclusion of which partisanship ran high...The second was a jig...
>
> After the second was disposed of, the final test was announced, which was to be in sacred music... With a few preliminaries he [the first contestant] struck into "Arkansas Traveller", throwing so many contortions into its execution, that it seemed as if life and liberty

AFTERNOON PERFORMANCE

(Begins at 2 o'clock)

PROGRAM

1. "Dixie," Played by all Fiddlers together.
2. "Sugar in the Gourd," prize 20 pounds sugar by J. W. Gilmore and J. J. Huey.
3. "Old Dan Tucker," prize a box of cigars by James Alison
4. "Arkansas Traveler," prize driving bridle by John Fry.
5. "Leather Breeches," prize a pair of trousers by Louisville Store
6. Banjo Contest—First prize a box of cigars by Perkins & Cron; second prize a year's subscription by THE EXAMINER.
7. "Fisher's Hornpipe," prize a half dozen cans of peaches by Franklin, Vaughan & Co.
8. "The Girl I Left Behind Me," prize Berkshire pig by Mrs. T. S. Ellis.
9. "Natchez Under the Hill," prize a hat by R. Beebe.
10. Left-handed Fiddlers' Contest—First prize fine umbrella by Robt. Guthrie & Co.; second prize a year's subscription by the Tennessean.
11. Jew's Harp Contest, prize a year's subscription by the Semi-Weekly News.
12. String Band Contest—First prize a box of cigars by Trousdale House; second prize a cake by Mrs. Zach Green.

EVENING PERFORMANCE: 7:30 o'clock.

1. Overture by prize band of afternoon contest.
2. Contest of Fiddlers, each one playing his own selection—First prize $15 in gold by Daughters of Confederacy and fiddle bow by Mrs. B. D. Bell; second prize $5 in silver by Farmers & Traders Bank; third prize $3 by McGlothin & Crafton and Person Bros. To the best Sumner county Fiddler $10 in gold by First Nat'l Bank.
3. "Hell Broke Loose in Georgia," prize a lamp by a merchant.
4. "Bill Cheatham," prize a dozen cans peaches by J. W. Drane and H. B. Lucus.
5. "Run, Nigger, Run" prize a pair of men's shoes by C. Levy & Bro.
6. French Harp Contest—First prize a box of cigars by H. R. Fidler; second prize 10 pounds of beef by P. L. Anderson.
7. "The Cackling Hen," prize Rocking Chair by A. M. Blue.
8. "Mississippi Sawyer," prize one hand saw by M. A. Ewing.
9. Oldest Fiddler, prize one barrel of Ideal Flour by Gallatin Mills.
10. Youngest Fiddler, prize one picture by Blackmore & Jackson.
11. Distribution of Prizes for Parade and Fiddler's Contest.
12. "Auld Lang Syne" played by all Fiddlers.

PRIZES OFFERED IN PARADE

Baby Pony Cart, prize box of candy by Foster & Brown.
Pony Cart, prize two pictures by R. G. Miller & Co.
Trap prize, pair of best ladies' shoes by The Hustler.
Buggy, Prize box of candy by Broderick & Taylor.
Carriage or Surrey, prize clock by W. F. Roth
Bicycle prize, medalion by A. R. Schell.
Merchants' Display, prize shaving set by W. J. Hancock.

All old-time Fiddlers of the world invited to enter contest. Admitted free and will be entertained by citizens of Gallatin. Accompaniest on stringed instruments allowed.

Admission 25¢. No Reserved seats.

Gallatin, Tennessee Contest Program—1899 (The Devil's Box magazine)

depended on his exertions...

[The second contestant] cut into "The Irish Washerwoman" with a great flourish, and in the refrain chanted an unitelligible gibberish like the yelping of a coyote."

Then the judges announced their decision.

" 'In regard to the last test, your judges cannot reach any decision, as the selections rendered fail to qualify under the head of -'

But two shots rang out in rapid succession across the street, and the crowd, including the judges and fiddlers, rushed away to witness the new excitement..."

Many of today's contests are better organized.

The accompanying program of a contest in Gallatin, Tennessee in 1899 indicates that the same tune was played by all fiddlers and the best rendition of each was accorded a prize. It is reasonable to assume that this practice was once common.

Apparently the first contests to have a strong impact in the Southeast were the Atlanta conventions from 1913 to 1935, sponsored at first by the Daughters of the Confederacy. It was a proving grounds for many fiddlers that went on to record classic renditions in the 1920's. Among the winners were Lowe Stokes (1924), John Carson (1927), Gid Tanner (1928) and A.A. Gray who recorded under the name Seven Foot Dilly (1929). Other well known participants included Arnim "Curly" Fox, Charley Bowman, Doctor Humphrey Bates and Clayton McMichen. The latter probably had the greatest contest success of any Southeasterner. He first won attention by finishing third at this convention at the age of thirteen. He won the National Association of Old Time Fiddlers Convention eight years in a row, 1925 to 1932.

At the first Atlanta convention there was a controversy whether to allow straw beating as an accompaniment (the rhythmic beating of thin sticks on the strings while the fiddler bows and notes). They were eventually allowed only in exhibition numbers. A cowbell was rung to signal the time limit though some fiddlers just treated it as accompaniment.

In the 1920's and '30's contests were frequent in the Southeast. Though documentation is scarce so far, the situation seems to have been similar in Texas. It even became something of a fad spearheaded by automobile kingpin, Henry Ford's attempt to bring back the 'old fashioned values' and counteract the evils of the Jazz Age. Ironically his industrial innovations were a major contributor to the breakdown of the rural culture that old time music represented to Ford. His nationwide 1926 contest, organized through his dealerships weeded out some 1,865 contestants and crowned Uncle Bunt Stephens of Tennessee as champion in the finals in Detroit, Michigan (though plenty of also-rans complained about the judging).

By the late twenties this fad faded while fiddle music was losing its commerciality in the Southeast in favor of the vocal-oriented music of Jimmy Rodgers and The Carter Family. As interest diminished so did support for contests. This was not true in Texas where the fiddle continued to be the main solo instrument in Western swing. So this state has had quite a few long running fiddle competitions.

The Gilmer Yamboree, started in 1935, normally requires only two hoedowns per contestant. In Halletsville's Texas State Championships only one hoedown is required on the first round. In the second a hoedown, waltz and tune of choice are played. A waltz and hoedown are played in the next round with no two fiddlers allowed to play the same tune. The winner and second place finisher get to play head-to-head against the previous champion. Here each have to play a breakdown, waltz, polka, schottische and rag. Athens, Munday, Rockwell, Weatherford, Terrell and Shamrock (held on Saint Patrick's Day) are other Texas towns that have had contests for quite a while.

Some of the famous frequenters of these competitions in the '30's and '40's were Cecil Brower, Hugh Farr, Spade Cooley and Southeasterners Arthur Smith, Curly Fox and Clayton McMichen.

Forty and fifty years ago it was pretty much no holds barred at these events. Eck Robertson was known to put a match under the treble side of his bridge to allow triple stops. Bob Wills' father, John was a frequent contestant. Bob's brother, Johnnie Lee

Wills states,

> "Papa, when he got to play a contest, he'd raise his bridge higher... and instead of tuning his fiddle to a natural 'A', he would tune it to a 'C' on a piano. That would make it... more brilliant and louder. There wasn't any microphone back then, and his fiddle was loud with its steel strings. "Lost Indian" he could holler the thing in high 'C' - - that's pretty high. The audience couldn't see if the fiddle was doing it or if he was hollering." (quoted by Charles Wolfe in The Devil's Box of June 1982)

Some contests were decided by audience reaction.

The current nationwide upsurge of contests owes much to such disparate items as the folk music revival, the popularity of bluegrass with its stress on fiddling, Benny Thomasson's move from Texas to Washington State in 1971 and, above all, the determination of fiddlers themselves to form fiddle associations. Of these, the Northwest branches have been most active in the past twenty years. All this is tied up with the popularization of returning to your roots and ecology coupled with conservatism and the idealization rural life. For some, old timey music symbolizes these ideals. In addition many Southerners have rejected the negative, unsophisticated image that the Nashville country-western business juggernaut has attached to traditional music.

The Weiser, Idaho contest became a focal point of the renaissance for other fiddlers by the 1970's. It has served as a model for contests around the country and has spread the Texas style through the participation of such as Byron Berline, Dick Barret, Benny Thomasson and Mark O'Connor. Even Eck Robertson participated, winning the Senior Division in 1962. The competition began in 1953 and became large enough to be called the National Old Time Fiddlers' Contest in 1963 (although naming of contests seems to be hyperbolic).

Weiser's success brought the realization to fiddlers across the country that they were not as isolated as they had thought. Besides additional associations this network of like-minded musicians has also resulted in an attempt to standardize the judging criteria.

While this has not been realized there are some basic rules that are generally accepted.

A hoedown and waltz are usually required, with some adding a tune of choice ie. a rag, polka, schottische or jig. Some ban post-1900 tunes but there is general agreement as to a loose definition of traditional-sounding tunes.

Trick fiddling, double shuffles and hokum tunes such as "Orange Blossom Special", "Listen to the Mockingbird" and "Black Mountain Rag" are taboo. Pizzicato and retuning the fiddle (called cross tuning or technically, scordatura) are also prohibited.

Excessive variation can result in a loss of points. Do not stray too far from home base and get too jazzy. These limits vary wildly, depending on the temperament of the officials.

Mark O'Connor, Benny Thomasson, & Jerry Thomasson at the White House in 1976.
(Photo courtesy of Benny Thomasson)

One or two accompanists are allowed which, for Texas style are now always guitarists. (Benny Thomasson's son, Jerry, has shown the effectiveness of a tenor guitar in this role.)

This gradual rules standardization and the tendency for previous winners to work as judges has led to the predominance of one style as the favorite in major contests, the Texas manner, represented by Benny Thomasson and his foremost pupil, Mark O'Connor. In fact it is sometimes now referred to as the national or super contest style. Some fiddle afficianados worry that this trend will hasten the extinction of the non-winning regional styles. Hopefully the resurgence of square and contra dances and the more frequent use of live music to accompany them will help keep the other styles vibrant. Then, there are contests that judge highest for local styles. Always scope out the judging routine before you play.

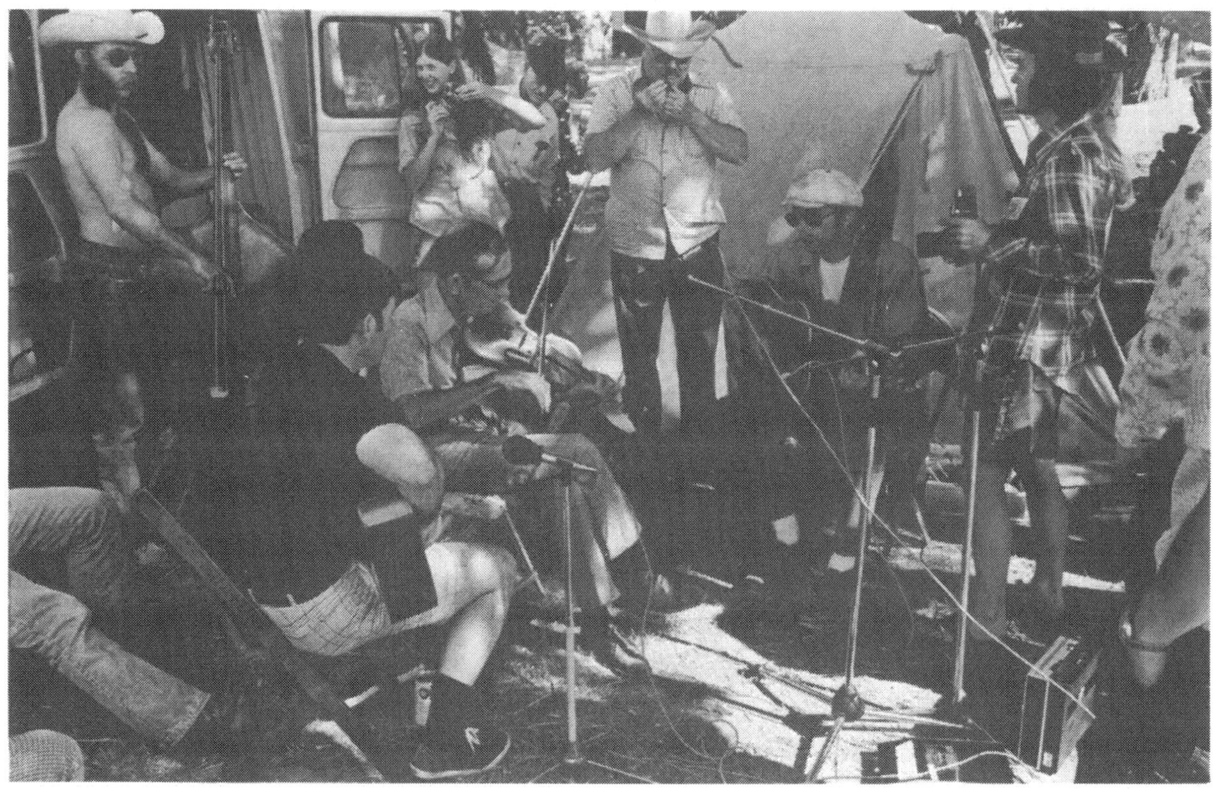

Weiser Jam—Benny Thomasson at center. (Photo by Brooks Otis)

ANNUAL

NATIONAL OLDTIME FIDDLERS' CONTEST

Weiser, Idaho 83672

Third Full Week in June

Amended 1979

GENERAL INFORMATION

PURPOSE — The original and continuing purpose of the National Oldtime Fiddlers' Contest is to help perpetuate the oldtime fiddling of pioneer America; to help develop a more genuine audience appreciation, understanding and participation; to preserve the oldtime fiddling tunes; to develop and encourage oldtime fiddlers' jam sessions and contests; to permanently record and display the history, relics and mementos of past oldtime fiddlers' art; and to acknowledge the present-day oldtime fiddlers who are helping to preserve the traditional expressions.

CONTESTS — Six Contests — GRAND CHAMPION, SENIOR, MEN, LADIES, JUNIOR and JUNIOR-JUNIOR Contests conducted annually. Contestant must be a resident of North America. (Rules available for specific information regarding each Contest.)

FIVE AREA WINNERS — The fiddler placing highest in National competition from each of the following five (5) areas will receive a Blaine Stubblefield Area Trophy. The areas are — NORTHWEST: (Alaska, Idaho, Montana, North Dakota, Oregon, South Dakota, Washington, Wyoming and the area in Canada lying west of the Saskatchewan and Manitoba borders); MIDWEST: (Canada, includes Manitoba and Ontario; Illinois, Indiana, Iowa, Kansas, Michigan, Minnesota, Missouri, Nebraska, Ohio and Wisconsin); NORTHEAST: (Connecticut, Delaware, Maine, Maryland, Massachusetts, New Hampshire, New Jersey, New York, Pennsylvania, Rhode Island, Vermont, Washington, D. C., and Quebec); SOUTHEAST: (Alabama, Arkansas, Florida, Georgia, Kentucky, Louisiana, Mississippi, North Carolina, South Carolina, Tennessee, Virginia and West Virginia); SOUTHWEST: (Arizona, California, Colorado, Hawaii, New Mexico, Nevada, Oklahoma, Texas and Utah).

JUDGING — Judging will be done by five (5) qualified judges and the high and low scores for each contestant at each appearance will not be used in calculating total points. Judging will be done by remote and no judge can see any contestant or hear an introduction or commentary. Contestant is identified only by number.

STOP WATCH — Stop watch will be used in the judging room to enable strict enforcement of the four minute rule.

CERTIFIED CONTESTS — The National Fiddlers' Certification and Advisory Council, with members from states throughout the nation, certifies local, regional and state contests that qualify. There are many advantages to being certified. Complete information available from the above Council, c/o Chamber of Commerce, Weiser, Idaho 83672. Please notify us of any contests in your area that would like to be certified and complete information will be sent.

NATIONAL FIDDLERS' HALL OF FAME — It pays tribute and honors oldtime fiddlers of renown and Certified Contest winners throughout the nation. It has established an archives of oldtime fiddling tunes, fiddling papers, notes and books; to be preserved for future generations. Old fiddles, fiddle mementos and pictures of honored fiddlers are on display. If you have any fiddling relics, mementos, recorded tunes, or information you wish to donate, please contact our committee, c/o Chamber of Commerce, Weiser, Idaho 83672.

PARADE — This is strictly an "oldtime parade" held on Saturday each year. In keeping with the general aims of our Contest, which is to perpetuate and promote oldtime fiddling, to collect and preserve authentic relics and mementos of the past; we are urging individuals and groups to restore and preserve antique items in the area as a continuing program. Fiddlers and other participants are invited to enter "oldtime" floats. Prizes are awarded in different categories.

DRESS — In keeping with the theme and purpose of the Contest, everyone is urged to wear "oldtime" dress of pioneer America. Prizes are awarded on this basis. However, since western dress is customary in this community, it will be acceptable if "oldtime" dress is not possible. Persons wearing beach wear, shorts, or sun swear will feel "out of place."

NOTE — All questions, decisions and plans will be governed by the over-all committee on the basis of our Purpose.

ANNUAL

NATIONAL OLDTIME FIDDLERS' CONTEST

Weiser, Idaho 83672

Third Full Week in June

GENERAL CONTEST RULES

Amended 1981

(Apply to National Grand Champion, Senior, Men, Ladies, Junior, Junior-Junior Contests)

1. Entry blank must be completed and entry fee paid before ENTRY DEADLINE.
2. ENTRY DEADLINE — Postmarked not later than Friday midnight, second week in June. Exception may be granted for due cause upon request to the Contest Chairman. We need pre-registrations to more effectively run the program. Money will be refunded to anyone who paid entry fee and cannot attend.
3. All commercial recording rights are reserved and shall become the property of the Weiser Chamber of Commerce, the non-profit and legal entity for the National Oldtime Fiddlers' Contest Committee. Signing of registration for the Contest shall waive such rights.
4. At registration, contestants shall draw for intial order of appearance for the first preliminary round. Judging Chairman in future rounds will draw before each round for new order of appearance. Announcements will be made of the drawings, and contestants must be ready to play when called. There will be neither seeding nor qualifying rounds in any contest. Any contestant registered and not playing will be eliminated from next year's Contest. Contestants badge and guest badge will be revoked for remainder of this year's Contest.
5. Contestants at each appearance must first play a hoedown; second, a waltz, and third, a tune of their choice **other than** a hoedown or waltz. No tune shall be played more than once during all appearances of a contestant. Four minute playing time will be strictly adhered to. Ten points will be deducted from total score for each 30 second interval or portion thereof.
6. If a string breaks, the FIDDLER will have the option to continue or stop at that point. If the tune is completed it will be judged as played. If the fiddler stops play he will be allowed to begin with that tune and complete his program.
7. Contestants may play without accompanist or with not more than two, but may register only one.
8. Any danceable folk tunes played in oldtime fiddle fashion are acceptable.
9. Contact microphones and amplified instruments will not be permitted.
10. No trick or fancy fiddling allowed during the contesting appearances. No cross tuning on stage.
11. No sheet music shall be displayed in the gymnasium while contesting.
12. Judging will be scored for oldtime fiddling ability, rhythm or timing, and tone quality. All scores will be accumulative. Points will be deducted for any violations of the above rules, No. 5 through No. 11 (inclusive).
13. Any contestant winning three consecutive years in the Grand National Division must either judge the next year's Contest or sit out the next year's Contest.
14. Any contestant winning three consecutive years in the Senior, Men, Ladies and Junior divisions automatically move into the Grand National Division. Any Junior-Junior winning three consecutive times will automatically move into the Junior Division.
15. Any protest must be submitted in writing to the Contest Chairman, and signed by not less than three contestants of the Contest involved, within three hours of protest occurrence.
16. All decisions of the Judges and of the Contest Committee will be final.

Please refer to each annual Contest Brochure and Program for information on various Contest prizes, trophies, entry fees, registration schedules.

SPECIAL CONTEST RULES

Contestants may enter only one of the following contests:

NATIONAL:	1. Contestants, open to all regardless of age. 2. Contestants may be of either sex.	**6 Rounds**
SENIOR:	1. Contestants must be at least 65 years of age. 2. Contestants may be of either sex.	**4 Rounds**
MEN:	1. Contestants must be at least 18 years of age. 2. Contestants — Men only.	**4 Rounds**
LADIES:	1. Contestants must be at least 18 years of age. 2. Contestants — Ladies only.	**4 Rounds**
JUNIOR:	1. Contestants must be less than 18 years of age. 2. Contestants may be of either sex.	**4 Rounds**
JUNIOR-JUNIOR:	1. Contestants must be less than 13 years of age. 2. Contestants may be of either sex.	**3 Rounds**

*****1979 JUDGING RULES AND REGULATIONS*****

I. GENERAL REGULATIONS

A. No electric amplification or drums will be permitted in any category.

B. Contestants in the Junior and Senior Fiddler categories will perform two tunes in the eliminations and three tunes in the finals. Beginner fiddlers and all bands will perfrom two tunes in the eliminations and finals. Contestants in all other categories will perform one tune.

C. Five finalists will be selected in the Beginner, Junior and Senior Fiddler categories. Four finalists will be selected in the band categories. First through fourth place winners will be selected from the first round of competition in all other categories.

D. Contestants performing in the individual performer categories may perform unaccompanied or with one or two accompanists.

F. Points earned in the eliminations in the: Beginner Fiddler, Junior Fiddler, Senior Fiddler, Bluegrass Band, and Old Time String Band categories will NOT carry over to the finals.

II. RESTRICTIONS ON PERFORMANCES IN CERTAIN CATEGORIES

A. Junior and Senior Fiddler Categories

Contestants will be required to play a waltz and a breakdown in both the eliminations and finals. Tunes performed in the eliminations MAY NOT be repeated in the finals. Three tunes will be required in the finals. The first tune played in the finals will be a "warm up" and WILL NOT be scored. ANY tune, played in ANY style may be used as the "warm up" tune. The following tunes will NOT be permitted when the contestant is being judged: ORANGE BLOSSOM SPECIAL, BLACK MOUNTAIN RAG, LISTEN TO THE MOCKINGBIRD.

III. JUDGING CRITERIA

A. Rhythm and Timing - 20 Points

The judges will look for even, consistent rhythm. Rushing, dragging, or unevenness in performance will result in lost points.

B. Creativity - 20 Points

The judges will look for variations, improvisations, and "good licks". However, these creative improvisations should not destroy the basic melody line. Repetitious performances (using the same licks over and over in the same tune) will result in lost points.

C. Authenticity and Taste - 20 Points

The judges will look for the selection of authentic performance styles. Indiscriminate use of variations that make the basic tune unclear (for example, the use of the "double shuffle" in the fiddle categories), and inappropriate modern licks will result in lost points.

D. Expression - 20 Points

The judges will look for the feeling that the contestant puts into his/her performance. Flat, mechanical, unfeeling performances will result in lost points as will excessive "showmanship."

E. Execution - 20 Points

The judges will look for tonal quality, clarity of notes, intonation, and general command of the instrument(s).

F. General Judging Considerations

Each of the above categories is worth a maximum of 20 points. Hence, each tune will have a maximum possible total of 100 points. Bands will be judged on the overall balance and command of all instruments. ALL performers are urged to consider placement of the instrument(s) in order to most effectively utilize the microphones. If the judges cannot hear an instrument, points will be lost. If an instrument is played too loud, distorted sound may result and points will be lost. In short, all the judges will be hearing is the sound that comes over the sound system!

Contest rules for Tennessee Valley Old Time Fiddler's Convention (Athens, Alabama)

With all the tension and competition that is concomitant with large cash prizes and many talented entrants, contests are succesful when the fiddlers enjoy themselves. Jamming and tune trading are the rule and friendly music cutting sessions are common between high-ranking rivals. Many thousands at Weiser, for example never listen to the contest at all.

When you really get involved with fiddling - the gradual working-up of tunes, the camaraderie of jam sessions and contests - it can be much more than the music itself. Read what Mark O'Connor has to say.

MARK O'CONNOR INTERVIEW

Mark O'Connor is acknowledged as the top Texas style fiddler of the day (though some Texans would probably disagree). The vitality, cleverness, high technical ability and controlled abandon of his playing have extended the somewhat shadowed boundaries of Texas and tradition-based fiddling in general.

Mark O'Connor at Benny Thomasson's Home—1970 (Photo by Marty O'Connor)

"He's plugged directly into the Great American Music Machine." - Matt Glaser

"For his age he is an old professional." - Stephane Grappelli

"I've met the greatest fiddlers in this nation, but to me Mark is the greatest one of all." - Benny Thomasson

I met Mark in the midst of a tour of one nighters with The Dregs, a rock band that concentrates on high energy instrumentals.

Stacy Phillips: How did you prepare for contests when you first started out?

Mark O'Connor: When I was twelve I practiced my butt off. That year I just stayed home from school. [His mother says that he managed to catch a continuous stream of suspicious colds to give him practice time.] My first year at Weiser I was eleven and I had this tape

Roy Lee Cowan
(Photo by Brooks Otis)

of gold... Benny Thomasson, Junior Dougherty, Roy Lee Cowan and J.C. Broughton in a fiddle jam session where they each played all these great tunes, and each took a long hack at them. That was so inspiring, to hear them yell at each other, "Yeah!". Man, there was something to work for! This is more than music, its a way of life for these fiddle contests. I went that summer just taping and taping - young friends of mine that were better than me. Right away I made friends with this really great fiddler, Loretta Brank. She studied under the same person that I did, Benny Thomasson. I just hung out with him as much as I could and he showed me everything. He lived about two hours from me.

Those summers would be fiddle contests every weekend somewhere in Washington, Oregon or Idaho, then during the winter it would be fiddle shows at least once a month and jam sessions another time of the month. Then I'd go down there [to Thomasson's house] and spend the day just learning these fiddle tunes and the style and that's how I got this wrist motion, all from Benny Thomasson. He was such a nice person to come up to and say, "Can you help me out?" and he would help you all day if you wanted. There aren't too many people that would do that.

SP: Could you say something about the way he varies a tune?

MO: There are certain notes he will touch on and quote, His quotes change all the time but you know its him. He never plays the same way. He just developed this style with certain notes and a certain type of controlled improvisation. A lot of fiddlers outside Texas don't have the knack for that control. They think, "I can do a little bit here." but it will be out of context and they won't hear it, maybe Texans would. Its amazing how many Texans have that contest fiddling down. Not too many are great technicians, all have that feel.

SP: Do you use mostly saw strokes in your contest playing?

MO: No. In hornpipes it would be mostly single notes, I think. In "Sally Johnson" there are a lot more little hooks in there so it wouldn't be all up and down. You want to get a feel happening but you don't want the same feel all the way through. Its one of the things I picked up by just watching.

There are a lot of times when there are two notes together. A neat thing is that most of the trills are on up bows. Most of the strokes are from the middle to close to the end.

SP: How did you prepare for a contest?

MO: Number one, I found out what were the prizes. (laughs) Number two, I found out the names of the judges. I've been around so I recognize names. If someone has a trip against my playing - if there are too many of those guys in the circle of judges, it might not be worth it to go because there's lots of prejudice among styles. When you get there you pick up on the drift. You get together [with other fiddlers]. Its friendly really.

They change the judges each year at Weiser. They try to get a Southern one [Oklahoma or Texas], an Eastern one and the rest from California, Washington, Canada maybe.

I went up to Canada one year and won the Calgary National Championship. Benny Thomasson was a judge, and two Canadians, so there's a complete split, but you had to play to those Canadians. You had to play the breakdowns a little faster. Play mostly single note waltzes because they don't like double stops. Just characteristics you pick up in Canada. I played them a little faster. They want to feel a dance, instead of a Texas waltz which is real slow. Then for third tunes I usually would play a polka because they don't have a fondness for rags. If you do play one its got to be stupidly slow.

SCORE SHEET CONTESTANT NO.

NATIONAL OLD TIME FIDDLE CONTEST
Weiser, Idaho

__ ROUND JUNE__19__ CONTEST______

POSSIBLE POINTS	OLDTIME ABILITY 40	RHYTHM 30	TONE 30	TOTAL 100
1. Hoedown				
2. Waltz				
3. Tune of Choice				
			GRAND TOTAL	

Judge____________________________

This is a replica of a judge's score sheet at Weiser, Idaho. The highest and lowest scores are thrown out.

When I judge the first thing I listen to is ability and how he is complementing his style. I know different styles although I can't play them all. So I listen for the style. Then I start picking down to rhythm and tone. But mainly its looking for the sound.

SP: What is the style that wins at Weiser?

MO: I won it the last three years. They asked me to judge this year but I don't think I can. It would be like a brain test. I'm not ready for six days, twelve hours a day. There are so many scratchers out there, 350 contestants. [The judges] are in a back room listening to monitors. [So they can identify the contestants only by number.]

You want to play as clean as possible. I mean super clean. Every note. I'd be mad at myself if I played one note that passed by. Every note right on top of the beat. That seems to do it. Other places in the country they don't care if its scratchy or rhythmic but at Weiser there's a thing about playing clean. Its better to play a simpler tune, well, not necessarily simpler but one that doesn't go as many places and play it man, right down the line. Like crash it.

There's a four minute time limit so there's no clapping between songs and that's weird You've got to go right into the waltz [after the breakdown]. Its a nerve-wracking experience.

[Mark returned to this topic later in our conversation, saying that with so many entrants you cannot play the whole tune anymore. Most contests have no time limit.]

SP: What's the physical situation where you're playing?

MO: Its a gymnasium with a stage right in the middle.

SP: So you're surrounded by the audience.

MO: Yeah. There are mikes coming down from the ceiling. The audience is sitting all around. You can hear a pin drop. You walk out and they say where you're from and you get the applause and you step up there, man its like a do-or-die thing. So many people lose it. So many people get off the stage like, crying because they couldn't handle the pressure. A lot of girls go straight to the bathroom. Some guys get sick and go off some place and can't stand the thought of seeing the cut. [the list of qualifiers for the next round] The older

I get, the more nervous I get because everyone expects me to finish in one of the top places all the time.

SP: What about the choice of tunes?

MO: You don't want to play anything that is the least bit controversial. You can play just about any rag, by Joplin or whatever. If you think you can play a tune better than anybody else, its safer to play tunes the judges recognize.

SP: How many rounds do they have at Weiser?

MO: Six for the Open. You can't repeat a tune so you go away playing eighteen, six waltzes, six breakdowns and six tunes of choice.

SP: Do they make the contestants play the same tune in any round?

MO: No, though in Crockett, Texas they have this year's champion play off with last year's champion. Both sit on stage, and they go, "Okay, polka." and one guy plays and then the next. "Okay, waltz." They do about six different tunes like that so you have to be prepared.

SP: Have there been any changes in contest fiddling, maybe technical ability or the style changing?

MO: The biggest change has been more younger people are getting better faster. Its being accessible to mass tapes and records of players and getting enthused about the competition of it all. A few years back at Weiser there were maybe 20 Juniors and ten Junior-Juniors. Now they have 50 to 60 Juniors and 30 to 40 Junior-Juniors. Tiny kids, its great.

[The conversation then turned to Benny Thomasson's background.] He didn't make his living fiddling. In the '50's he was considered a genius. I've heard tapes, incredible playing. He played like he does now but all the technique and tone and pitch were there - speed and fluid. Its heavier than anything I've heard.

SP: Any chance of that stuff coming out on record?

MO: No, all these tapes are poor quality of jam sessions. A lot were made in this body shop with people wrecking cars in the background. Benny has a tape of a contest he was in, Athens [Texas] in 1950 or something and they're going, "Oh no! We got the wooorrld champion fiddler up here." and people start screaming. It sounds like a football game. He gets up there and plays cross-key "Black Mountain Rag"—you can do anything in Texas—and the announcer, during the tune, was yelling, "Get him off the stage!

He's too good!" and he kept fiddling.

If you go down to Crockett, Texas its still like the old days down there. The old guys hang out. Fiddling is a sport. They're yelling, "Go, Go, Go!" Its a way of life. You stay up all night and get drunk, go to different people's houses and play all night. Benny was part of that.

Benny Thomasson and Major Franklin were quite a rivalry back thirty years ago, where they would sometimes tie in a contest and have tie after tie after tie in playoffs. Usually Benny won because he knew more tunes. Major developed the Texas style along with Benny but had a different way to approach it. He's more of a choppy type player and plays more syncopations and stuff. He was a genius too. They would always be one and two in the contests.

SP: Any names before those two?

MO: Eck Robertson. Man I wish I could go back to those days. They had contests in the '40's, Benny played against Eck and they would tie. Another guy was Bryant Houston. I think he wrote most of "Limerock". [Mark had played this during the concert.]

February 21, 1982

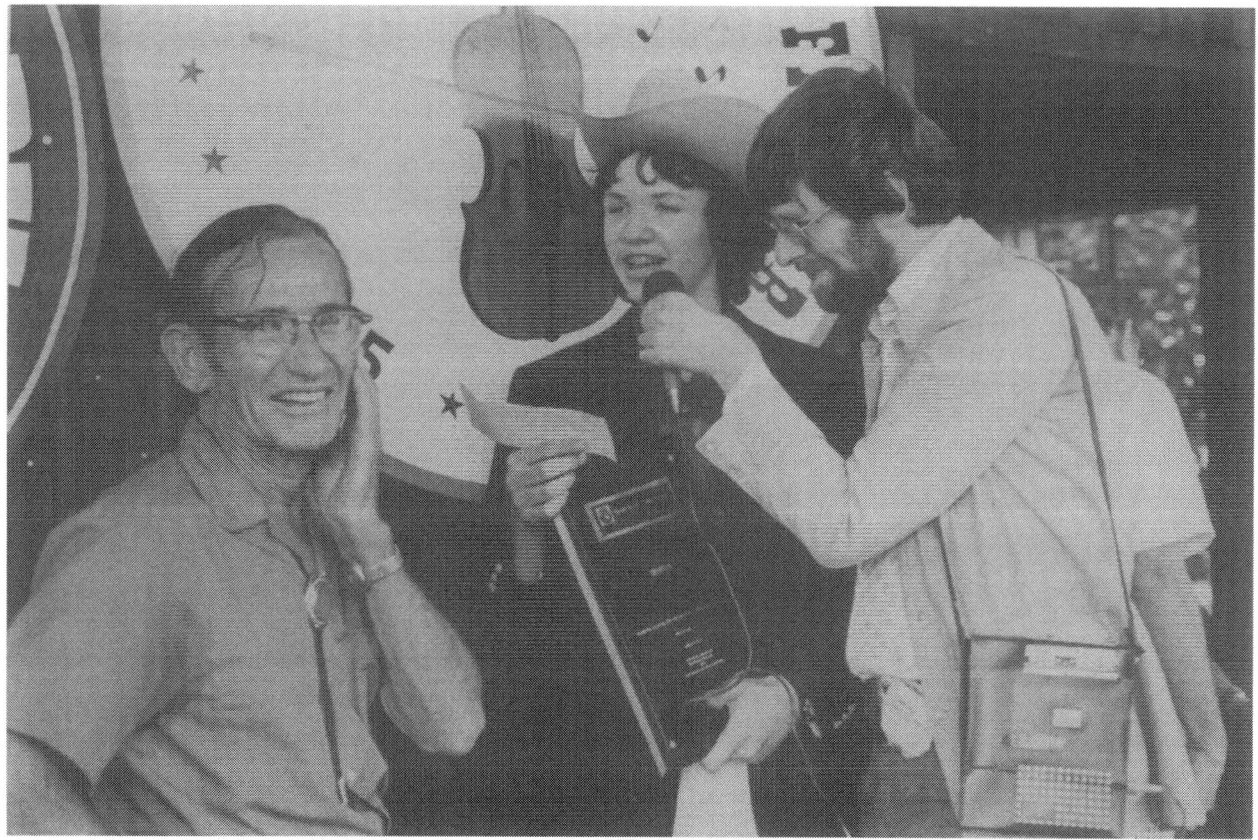

Mark O'Connor's first Grand Masters' Victory—1975. Benny Thomasson shares the moment. (Photo by Marty O'Connor)

Among Mark's many victories are three at Weiser's Nationals (1979-80-81) and three at Nashville's Grand Masters (1975-80-81), the most prestigious contests in America. His parents' home is bursting with his many trophies for his fiddle, guitar and mandolin playing.

Here are the tunes Mark O'Connor played when winning at Weiser in 1981. The order for each round is hoedown, waltz and tune of choice.

round 1 - "Bill Cheatem", "Chancellor's Waltz", "Jesse Polka"
round 2 - "Wagoner Hornpipe", "Roxanna Waltz", "Clarinet Polka"
round 3 - "Peaches and Honey", "Goodnight Waltz", "Allentown Polka"
round 4 - "Uncle Herman's Hornpipe", "Kentucky Waltz", "Calgary Polka"
round 5 - "Sally Goodin", "Ookpik Waltz", "Johnson's Rag"
round 6 - "Hell Among the Yearlings", "Skater's Waltz", "I Don't Love Nobody"

Weiser, 1978—Mark O'Connor (2nd place), Herman Johnson (1st place), Junior Daugherty (3rd place).
(Photo by Brooks Otis)

BENNY THOMASSON INTERVIEW

Benny Thomasson has to be the most influential Texas fiddler. The names he mentions in this interview are some of the best around, and all owe much to his style. He was raised in Gatesville, Texas where people like Eck Robertson and Lefty Franklin often visited his father, Luke, author of the singular fiddle tune "Midnight on the Water".

He has won the Crockett World Championships in 1955, 56 and 57 and Weiser in 1974 as well as his share of Gilmer, Athens and other Texas contests. His house, like Mark O'Connor's, is filled with trophies.

Benny Thomasson moved to Washington State expecting that his days of public fiddling were over. To his surprise he was discovered by the fiddlers of the Northwest who took his style to their hearts and bows.

Down a back road and left at the black walnut trees, I came upon Benny picking peas in his garden.

Stacy Phillips: Please talk about how the tunes have changed.

Benny Thomasson: There's been quite a change. Back when I started they had only two part tunes, [The four minute rule at Weiser is bringing some of these back.] and that was it. And too, they've changed the rules so much that its altogether different now to what it was then. They used to do "Chinky Pin" and "Turkey in the Straw" a whole lot, and old tunes that didn't have any color to them. [Now] more tunes are played in 'A' that's got a lot of volume, colors and moves to them.

In the older days when I began to come up I took these old tunes and began to build different sections to them. Like there would be two parts, well I'd add another, it would be the same part but in a different position. The tunes finally got to where they were sort of hard to handle. The harder to handle, the harder it was for the next guy to do. (laughs)

SP: Could you comment on the difference between old time and contest fiddling?

BT: The old timey fiddling that they try to hang onto nowadays, its alright. Its good to listen to but we take those same tunes and just weave a web around them and make it come out real pretty. But it seems to me that they don't like that much. (laughs). I never was used to them making these accusations about the changes we made. We didn't know where the tunes came from or what it was. We just played them and kept adding to them until we got it to suit ourselves.

On alot of these tunes you've got to use a certain bow to make it sound right. You make two or three notes in a stroke, sort of drag the bow. Then you go back to fiddling.

SP: When you first started adding things did any of the judges give you a hard time?

BT: Well, to start with they did but after I got used to it I gave them a hard time because I was going a little ahead of them every year. We'd play "Grey Eagle" or something like that at a contest and I'd play it one year with a little change from the year before. Next I'd play a little different version to it. It got to where it had several parts.

SP: Do you remember any tricks fiddlers used to impress judges?

BT: Old Eck Robertson, He'd play a tune, he'd sing along with it. That was his deal. There were more fiddlers that came around later that did ["Listen to] the Mockingbird" and they'd put birds and all that stuff into it. Made it real nice, I liked it. Of course the judges didn't like it see 'cause it was getting so far ahead of the guys that never did it. Before cross tuning went out, now they retuned fiddles. When I was a young fellow most everybody cross-tuned. But when it got to later years the younger ones came up that didn't cross-tune, they were raising cane about it you know and stopped all cross-tuning. There were certain pretty powerful fiddlers who didn't cross-tune. They didn't want noone else to because it sounded so much better you see. I can play either way as far as it goes. Major Franklin was one that would stomp you to death nearly if you would. (laughs) They'd come around and thump [pluck] your fiddle to see if you had it cross-tuned.

"Black Mountain Rag" and stuff like that, show tunes, they finally cut that out.

SP: So when you first started fiddling they did allow most anything.

BT: Sure, anything you played, it didn't make any difference. You could play "Pop Goes the Weasel" and put it on top of your head and under your legs. They might win the contest doing that. What they did was to weed it down to where actual fiddling of the old tunes had to be done in the manner of a straight key, with no trick fiddling, no plucking, no hokum.

SP: Were you ever penalized for something tricky?

BT: No, that wasn't what I was doing. You could always figure out who the judges were and I'd always watch it real close not to get too far out of line.

Georgia Slim Rutland use to tune his fiddle higher [to make it brighter], that was alright. They never said anything about that. Incidentally, he was a good fiddler, a great one. He came to my house many times, him and Howdy Forrester. Them boys were both fine fiddlers. I taught them a lot of stuff, "Say Old Man Can You Play the Fiddle", somewhere in the 1940's. They were at my house every other night or two.

SP: Did they enter any contests?

BT: Yeah. I don't remember but one contest Howdy Forrester was in. We knew it was a put-up thing because Slim was a radio man. They knew him all over the country. It was between him and Eck Robertson in Dallas. It was a big contest. Old Georgia Slim came out on top. Eck played more old time stuff. He played that "Sally Goodin" better than anybody else in the world.

SP: How were these contests, the Dallas one or the real small ones, how were they set up?

BT: They hardly had a stage. Maybe they'd build one in a furniture store. The first contest I ever played in was in one. I won a five dollar gold piece, first prize. No microphones. The judges were ordinary people picked out of the crowd.

SP: How about the big contests?

BT: They had regular judges there you know. They were supposed to be fiddlers but some weren't.

We'd be fiddling together under a shade tree and they'd call us and call use to take our turn. If we were playing we'd keep on going.

SP: I was told that at some contests the judges would come on stage as you played.

BT: Yeah. I've had a lot of people do that. Had a contest in east Texas one time, Gilmore, that used to be the biggest contest there was in Texas and all the judges would come up and swarm around you, five judges, and look right down on what you were doing. (laughs)

Every move you made.

In Gilmore they had an outside stage. The street's out in the front. They had a carnival and everything during the fair. That was the best I went to down there I guess.

SP: How many tunes did you have to play?

BT: You had a breakdown, a waltz and tune of choice. You could play anything for the tune of choice. It was alright to retune for that. I played "Black Mountain Rag" alot of times down there.

SP: Mark told me about a contest where the judge yelled out, "This guy's too good!"

BT: (laughs) Yeah! This was in New Mexico I think. I was out there just bowing like everything and thought I was getting along real good. I was getting after it, see. I never got a point. They figured I was a professional. Never played professionally in my life.

SP: You and Major Franklin are given a lot of the credit for the new style of Texas playing. Could you tell me a little about him?

BT: Well, he had a little different style but it was a great style. He never made a move unless he knew exactly where he was going. He noted clear.

Once I was playing "Sally Goodin" at a contest and Major, while I was playing, he jumped in there started playing back of us. (laughs) He just went wild. He forgot what was going on. Judge comes over and says "Hey Major, he's playing in the contest." He didn't realize it. It was a lot of fun back in them days.

SP: Did you get together with him outside the contests?

BT: Oh yeah, gosh, I knew him like a book. I used to visit him all the time. I only lived about 100 miles from him [Denison, Texas]. I went to his house and he said I want you to meet some neighbors, and he said, "I want to tell you something. This is the best fiddler in the world - in the world!" It kind of knocked me for a roll. He never bragged on anybody. That sounded awful good to me coming from him because he said exactly what was in his mind.

When he went to fiddling he wanted everyone to fiddle just right, not to be sidewinding nowhere.

SP: How about playoffs?

BT: One night me and Ol'Major, we played one tune each at a time. We fiddled eight or ten tunes before they decided. I think they were holding on for more people to come. I won that contest incidentally. At the World Championship in Crockett you'd play against the previous champion. If you won three years straight you were the world's champion. I was the first. Texas Shorty was the next. I taught him all during that time.

SP: How do you prepare a waltz?

BT: Stay in line with the original. The double stops and harmony have got to be right on the money. Your slides, move it down just like they're supposed to go. You don't just 'jobble' up a waltz.

SP: Do you use a lot of vibrato?

BT: In the hoedowns you don't. In a waltz you use a slight bit of vibrato.

SP: Where did you use to play besides contests?

BT: I played for dances two nights a week at a hall in town and I played popular music there, "Sweet Sue" and stuff like that, "Tuxedo Junction". We had a bass fiddle, two guitars, four or five string banjo and a piano. For the squares we'd play a hoedown. We might play a little faster for the dance than contests.

SP: Could you name some of the other champion fiddlers from Eck Robertson's generation?

BT: I could name a few that were before Eck. There was Matt Brown. He was the one that wrote "Done Gone" and "Kelly Brown" or "Kelly's Waltz". My daddy played with Matt Brown. I met an old boy down in Dublin, Texas that played with both those boys, and he showed me some stuff that they did that was out of this world. Lum Sellers was another good fiddler. He played "Limerock" and things like that. Bryant Houston was the one that Lum Sellers taught. When "Limerock" first started out there wasn't nothing to it. We made it into a composed-sounding piece.

SP: Could you name some fiddlers besides Major Franklin that were your biggest competitors?

BT: Norman Solomon, Vernon Solomon, Lewis Franklin, Dick Barrett, all them guys. Major was my worst competitor. You had to be careful what you were doing when you got up there. (laughs) He was a great old fiddler.

E.J. Hopkins was good, and Johnny Gimble. Me and Johnny would get in a room up there and I'd play a breakdown and Johnny would come back and play a hot fiddle part. Didn't matter what it was.

SP: Who's winning down there now?

BT: Shorty wins and Jimmy Don Bates. There are good fiddlers there just like back in the old days. Carl Hawkins, just a kid when I left. Terry Morris is a great fiddler, and Dale Morris. I taught old Dale to play.

SP: Can you remember your first impression of Mark O'Connor?

BT: I began to teach him when he was just a kid. I saw him in a corner down at a little old contest someplace. He was trying to get "Sally Goodin". I showed him the whole part and he got it. That's what impressed me. Then he started to come to my house. He'd come and stay a few days at a time. I tell you, you could teach him four or five tunes a day and he would never forget them. I don't guess that there's a musician that ever lived that I know of that could compare with him. A great musician. I did have a little to do with straightening him out on his hoedowns.

SP: When you were learning to play did you hear any Southeastern fiddling?

BT: Yeah, I listened to Clark Kessinger when I was a kid. He sent me a tape one time. Another prime fiddler was Ervin Solomon, that's Vernon and Norman Solomon's dad. He played the old time style. He made a record with [Joe] Hughes. That record didn't do him justice.

SP: How come you didn't take up the fiddle as a profession?

BT: I had a few kids and you can't get away. They probably wouldn't have been worth killing now if I'd left. (laughs)

SP: I read a story about when you thought you were ready for the Dallas contest and didn't place.

BT: Yeah, I thought I was a pretty good fiddler. These boys have got to wake up in the morning to beat me. I laid "Grey Eagle" in there. They never knew I was there, and that's when I started fiddling. That was the contest that Georgia Slim won.

Shorty Louder [spelling?] was a good fiddler and he was there. He'd go around with his fiddle under his chin, by himself, saying, "Ain't a man in the world that can beat this." (laughs)

SP: It seems that Texans have a special feeling for fiddling.

BT: You might call it that. I've lost a lot of crops playing the fiddle. (laughs) I've stayed in the bathroom sometimes all night working on one tune, getting it to where it'd be presentable. Better than last year.

July, 21, 1982

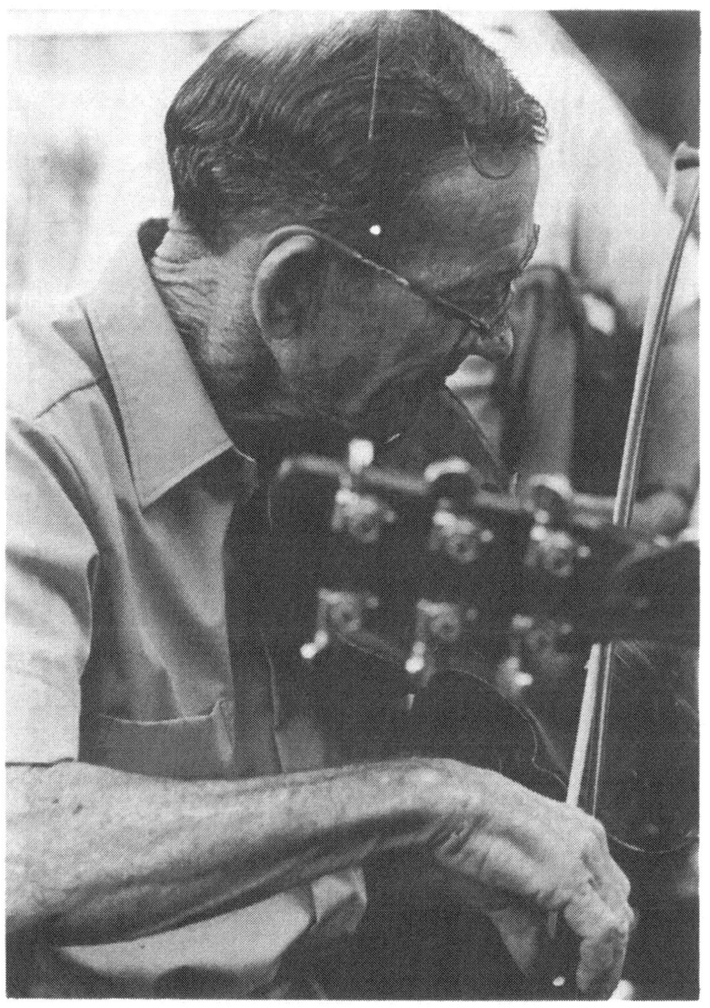

Benny Thomasson (Photo by Brooks Otis)

HOEDOWNS

Here is a goodly selection of breakdown types of all shapes and sizes. In some I clump all the variations of each section together to ease comparison. Others are arranged as they might be played on stage, with the usual order of sections, and that order repeated as many times as there are interesting variations.

Most are recognizably from the Scots-Irish tradition and the titles are shared by most fiddling areas of the United States.

Texas Shorty at Dick Barrett's Invitational Fiddle Contest—Durant, OK; November 1978. Photo by Marty O'Connor

WAGONER

Let us blast off with a standard number, "Wagoner", (also called "Texas Wagoner" or "Tennessee Wagoner") probably named for the driver of the old, ox-driven Conestoga wagons.

This tune started out as a typical old time two part tune, with a high strain (the first section of this arrangement) followed by a low one, mostly played on the bottom two strings. Texans altered the low part, eventually transmuting it into an entirely new section by the addition of a D7 chord.

I have grouped similar strains together. When performed two high parts are followed by two low ones. By the sixth version of the first section (measure 41) the melody is dropping out of sight. The sixth through tenth versions stress bow rocking between the 'e' and 'a' strings. These impart some nice rhythmic accents while the last measure of each returns to the melody. The eleventh and twelfth variations (starting on measure 81) bow rock on the 'a' and 'd' strings.

Measures 97 to 120 are examples of the original low part still played by Southeasterners, and measure 121 introduces the Texas mutation. As this part is varied it loses its 'low' character and winds up in third position. The last two strains demand some difficult hand position changes but, in context, sound quite spectacular and are worth some effort.

The main sources for this construction of "Wagoner" are Benny Thomasson, Mark O'Connor and Sam Bush. Sam is the moving force of The New Grass Revival and, in his younger days won the Junior Division at Weiser. He plays fiddle tunes with a nice amalgam of Southeastern and Southwestern styles. A possibly apocryphal story goes that he refused to cut his hair for the Weiser victory photo, so a blank frame was placed in their hall of fame.

The tempos of the versions I have heard vary from MM=112-120.

C
G7
C
G7
C
9
17
25
33

41
49
57
65
73

81
89
98
108
118
(1)
C
(0)
D7
G7
C
F
G7

128
C
138
148
157
(2)
(1)
167
(1)
(1)

TOM AND JERRY

"Tom and Jerry" appears to be of Texas origin and is related to "Sally Goodin" and "Grey Eagle Hornpipe". I have arranged the sections in the order they might be played.

The two variations of the first section (measures 1-16) are quintessential Texas fiddling. 'a' and 'e' drones abound, with frequent slurred notes, (but not in single shuffle style) and a few blue notes. The second section (measures 16-29) is similar to a part of "Grey Eagle". Follow the bowing notation for the proper feel, and do not let the bow leave the strings.

The 30th measure begins a low strain that, as usual, does not stay low very long. A typical key of 'A' high part (in third position) begins with measure 46.

Starting another go-round of the first section, measure 62 employs the bowing style of Major Franklin. He occasionally plays with a gentle staccato ie. his bow does leave the strings. When used with reserve this is a striking touch. Remember, not too staccato. The effect can be acheived by using very short strokes and gently bouncing the bow.

Measure 83 begins a high version of the second section, while measure 99 initiates a fourth variation of the low section with a slide into an octave 'a' double stop. The whole shebang ends with a high strain.

Benny Thomasson and Major Franklin are the major contributors to this arrangement which is usually played close to MM=116.

I have used an example of the Texas accompaniment style for the chording. (Thanks to Russ Barenberg) 'A9/C#' means an 'A9' chord with a 'c#' note in the bass. The typical idea is to have an ascending bass line at least part of the way through the chord changes.

The fourth measure could be played as all 'E7'. An alternative progression for the first part is placed between measures 62 and 66. This also works well on the last eight measures of the piece. Let your guitarist (or pianist) help you with these decisions.

Once you get the idea, there are a myriad of small variations that can be made in the chording to this tune as well as hoedowns like "Leather Britches", "Sally Johnson" and "Sally Goodin".

You can always use the old style chords which, for "Tom and Jerry" go something like

| A | A | A | E7 | A | A | A | E7 A |

A
A9/C♯
D
D♯°
A
(A♯°)
Bm7
E7
A
A9/C♯
D
D♯°
A
A/F♯
8
E7
A
14
A
D
E7
A
22
D
E7
A
1.
2.
30

38
46
54
62
71
staccato
A
F♯m
A
E7
1.
2.
E7
A
A
D
A
E7

79
A
D
E7
A
87
95
103
111

ACE OF SPADES

"Ace of Spades" is a little different than the run-of-the-mill hoedown. It has three distinct parts (ie. with very different chord progressions) and it is even kind of pretty.

The first section features short, fast notes while the second opens with some extended double stops and long bow. The third part switches to the key of 'E'. Watch for the added 'd#' in the key signature. In the 25th measure the cycle recommences with the first part.

The main sources for this rendition are Benny Thomasson and Dick Barret. The latter is a Texan who moved to Montana where he runs a school for fiddlers. He has been a consistent high finisher in big contests, winning Weiser in 1971, '72, '75 and '76, the Tennesse Valley Old Time Fiddle Convention in 1971 and the Grand Masters' in 1973.

This tune is played on the slow side, the tempos I have heard being close to MM=110.

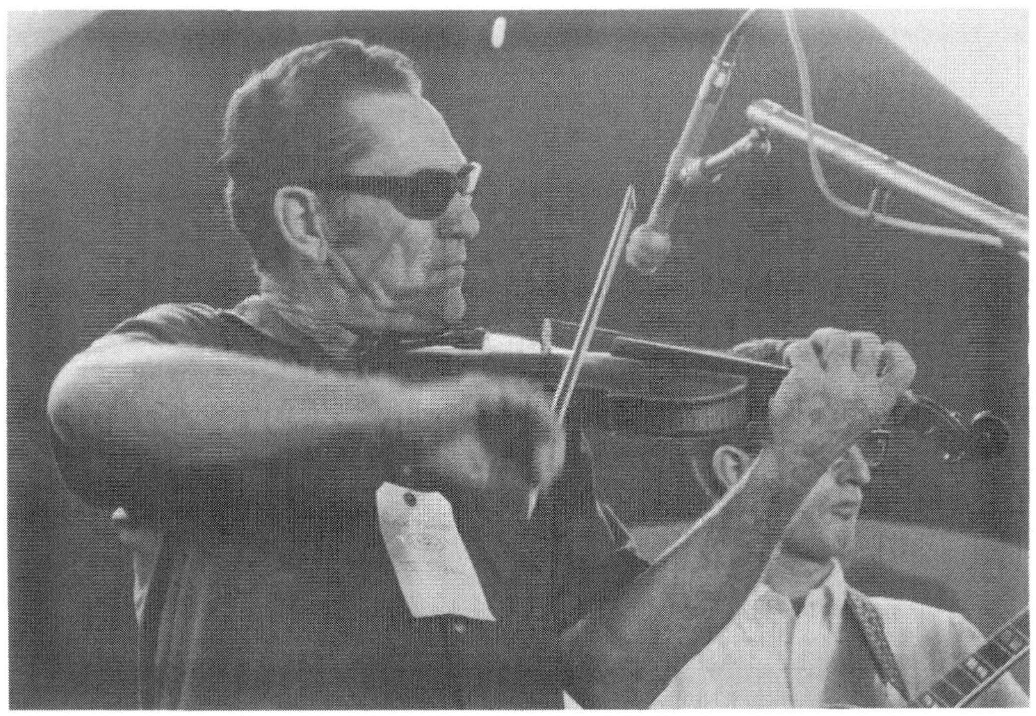

Dick Barret (Courtesy of the Devil's Box)

ACE OF SPADES

E7
A
32
E7
1. A
2. A
A
D
E7
A
40
D
E7
A
E
B7
E
48
B7
1. E
2. E
A
E7
A
56
E7
A

FORKED DEER

Now a stopover in the key of 'D' for the king of the wooded glen, the rampant "Forked Deer". This arrangement is mostly taken from the playing of Major Franklin, Sam Bush and J.T. Perkins. Perkins is from Arab, Alabama and, as a youth, travelled with early country music great, Riley Puckett. His Southeastern base has been strongly impregnated by the Texas style. He has won the Athens, Alabama Tennessee Valley Old Time Fiddlers' Convention several times. A fiddler deserving of greater recognition, he usually adds some interesting ideas to his versions.

This is a two section tune, the second starting on an 'A' chord. Notice there are three different chord progressions that have developed for this part. It is the folk process in action. The first of these starts in the 10th measure, the second on the 34th and the third at measure 66. The final two variations of the second section, starting with measure 98, have the same progression as those at measure 34. It is a good idea to stick with one of these possibilities per rendition. Accompanists tend to resent too many surprises. You can always change the others around a bit to fit the progression you favor.

Measures 50-81 show a strong Major Franklin influence, especially the staccato passages. (See "Tom and Jerry")

Another possiblity for the chord progression of the first section follows.

||D Bm| Em A7 | D Bm | Em A7 | D Bm | Em A7 | D G | A7 D||

I have heard renditions vary between MM106-118.

FORKED DEER

34
A
D
A
D
G
A7
D
42
50
D
G
D
A7
D
G
D
G
A7
D
58
66
staccato
A
stacc.
D
G
A7
D

74
stacc.
stacc.
82
D
G
D
A7
D
G
D
G
A7
D
90
D
G
98
A
3
3
D
A
D
G
A7
D
3
106
3

LEATHER BRITCHES

"Leather Britches" is a typical one chord fiddle tune that has been extended, contorted and generally put through the wringer by merciless fiddlers and their accompanists.

The first sixteen measures are two variations of the basic theme, the first based on Howdy Forrester and the second on Benny Thomasson. Howard 'Howdy' Forrester is from Hickman County, Tennessee and, while in his 'teens was fortunate to play in a band with Arthur Smith and Georgia Slim Rutland, two of the most influential fiddlers of the 1930's and '40's. The band moved to Texas and there he was influenced by the Franklins and Benny Thomasson. When he moved to Nashville to play with Roy Acuff he returned with a strong vein of Texas style permeating his playing. His fiddle tune arrangements amazed the Southeast fiddle world and brought the Texas contest style to their attention. Other contributors to this setting of "Leather Britches" include J.T. Perkins and Dick Barret.

The 17th measure ushers in the shadowy second section. What is it's melody and chord progression? It is pretty enigmatic.

Measure 33 initiates two high variations of the first section followed by two more of the low strain, though the difference between the high and low themes gets pretty arbitrary.

After another second section at measure 65 an interesting third position modification begins. This features some nice 'g' string drones and a |D7 A7|D7 G|progression at the end. A similar variation begins at measure 105 but without the 'A7' chord. A third position second section kicks off at measure 121, and the two final high strains are also mostly in this position.

An alternative for the chords of the third and fourth measures of the first section is | G/D G#°| Am7 D7 | . With a 'C' chord appearing in the seventh measure it might sound better to play just 'G' in measures five and six. The chord situation in this tune is really in a shocking state.

Tempos for this tune range from MM-115-125.

LEATHER BRITCHES

33
41
49
57
65

73
(1
0)
G9/B
C
C#°
G
G/E
D7
G
G9/B
C
C#°
D7
A7
D7
G
81
(0)
(0)
89
G
G9
C
C#°
G
D7
(G)
G
G9/B
C
C#°
C/E
G
D7
G
97
(4)

105
3
113
121
130
140

BLACKBERRY BLOSSOM

The possibilities for tasty variations within the framework of Texas fiddling are numerous indeed, as this 200+ measure compilation of "Blackberry Blossom" attests. From the straight-ahead tune to the near hysteria of measures 143-144 and 182-186 and onward to the dissonance of the 191st measure, the list of thrills and chills is lengthy indeed.

I have given a couple of chord progressions for each of the tune's two sections. The first section's chord choices (starting at measures 1 and 43) are pretty much interchangeable. For the second (Em) part, the first progression works best in measures 10-18. All other second section variations use a B7 chord in their fourth measures, even with the somewhat dissonant 'g' and 'd' naturals played over it.

Some of the wilder parts might cause problems with some judges, but the 'straighter' ones are a short course in Texas contest improvisation. I have drawn from the playing of Mark O'Connor, J.T. Perkins, J'anna Jacoby and James "Texas Shorty" Chancellor for this rendition. Jacoby won the Grand Masters' Contest as a teenager in 1978. Her playing is strongly influenced by Mark O'Connor. Chancellor was the original 'enfant terrible' of Texas fiddling, winning the first of three consecutive World Championships at Crockett in 1959, at the age of sixteen. Three time winners were retired from competition at that time. He spent much of his youth travelling from contest to contest developing his skills and reputation as the heir to Benny Thomasson.

In 1979 Texas Shorty won the Grand Masters, and a change in the Crockett rules allowed him to enter again and win in 1980 and '81. One of the unknown greats of the fiddle world.

"Blackberry Blossom" is usually played at around MM=120.

BLACKBERRY BLOSSOM

33
Em
B7
Em
41
G
C
D7
G
G
D7
C
G
C
G
D7
G
D7
C
G
49
C
G
D7
G
57

65
1.
2.
73
81
89
97

105
1.
2.
113
121
129

137
145
153
1.
2.
161
169

177
1.
2.
185
1.
2.
191
199

BILLY IN THE LOWGROUND

"Billy in the Lowground" is supposedly named after a fiddler who falls into a sinkhole and fiddles for help. It happens every day in Texas. Like "Blackberry Blossom" this version presents a broadside of the musical ideas that define Texas fiddling.

This is a two part, low strain-high strain tune with onechord structure. As the variations progress the difference in strains is swallowed by a welter of notes. To break up this simple chord pattern I have introduced a mutant strain into the proceedings starting at measure 169. The 'F' chord comes as a great relief. This section has an odd number of measures and also has a number of odd measures. Watch out for the one in 2/4.

It is back to the usual in measure 182. The octave 'c' slide need not be rushed. It can sound a bit trombone-like. The last three variations return to the basic melody.

This version derives mostly from Mark O'Connor, Major Franklin, Benny Thomasson, Texas Shorty, Terry Morris and Junior Dougherty. Terry Morris is a relative newcomer from Fort Worth, Texas who learned the basics from Benny Thomasson recordings. He won in Crockett in 1975 and '76, in Nashville in 1976 and the Texas Old Time Fiddle Association Championship at Burnett in 1975 and '76. By now he has probably won a bushel more.

Junior Dougherty, of Las Cruces, New Mexico is a perennial high finisher at Weiser and has won the Arizona and New Mexico State Championships.

The tempos for this arrangement range from MM=110 to 120.

C
Am
C
Am
G7
C
9
17
25

33
41
49
57
65

73
81
89
97
105
(4) (0)

113
121
129
137
145

153
161
169
Am
C
177
F
C
Am
C
Am

186
C
Am
G7
C
194
202
210
218

GOLDEN EAGLE HORNPIPE

Texans tend to play hornpipes with very few tied notes. The melody is usually comprised of a series of arpeggiated chords. "Golden Eagle" is a rare one I learned from a tape of Benny Thomasson. It was done at about MM=106.

Benny Thomasson (Photo by Brooks Otis)

GOLDEN EAGLE HORNPIPE

ALFIE'S HORNPIPE

When a contest has several rounds you will hear a hornpipe or two in the hoedown category. I learned "Alfie's Hornpipe" from the fiddling of Joe Panczerowski, a Northwesterner.

Watch the key change starting in the 10th measure. I heard this tune at about MM=116.

SOUVENIR PROGRAM

11th ANNUAL

Tennessee Valley

OLD TIME FIDDLERS' CONVENTION

Jacky, come give me your fiddle,
If ever you mean to thrive.
Nay, I'll not give my fiddle
To any man alive.

If I should give my fiddle,
They'll think that I'm gone mad,
For many a joyful day
My fiddle and I have had.

Athens State College

ATHENS, ALABAMA
SEPT. 30 - OCT. 1, 1977

(Courtesy of The Devil's Box magazine)

ALFIE'S HORNPIPE

SALLY JOHNSON

Here is a marathon exposition of every permutation you could ask for, in what is basically a two chord, one part tune. I have culled ideas from Benny Thomasson, Mark O'Connor, Terry Morris, Texas Shorty, Dick Barret, Vernon Solomon, J'Anna Jacoby and Herman Johnson. There are a lot of trophies represented in that list.

Vernon Solomon is a winner of the Grand Masters' (1972) and is the son of Ervin Solomon. Herman Johnson is an Oklahoman who has won at Weiser in 1968, '69, '77 and '78 and at Nashville in 1974. This is only a short catalogue of the championships credited to these two fiddlers.

There are perhaps six different strains I have noticed and I have grouped the different examples of each together. The first hovers around high 'g'. The second strain gravitates towards middle 'g' beginning at the 41st measure. By measure 113 this distinction breaks down and the next five versions are improvisations that occasionally bear elements from several motifs. An offspring of the second strain, reminiscent of "Leather Britches" appears in measure 153 with a 'g' drone and a long pinky stretch to hit a middle 'd' on the third string in measures 153 and 155. This stretch can be avoided by playing the 'd' on the 'a' string and omitting the drone.

Three examples of a descendant of this strain appear from measures 169 to 192. They display a long bow first measure and some third position playing. Samples of a high strain, taking place mostly in third position, extends between measures 193 and 216.

The low strain goes from measure 217 to 256. The amount of 'd' string drone is a matter of taste.

The sixth variation starts off with the bow jumping back and forth between the bottom and top two strings. The last two sections return to the first strain.

In places where there are at least two consecutive triplets, the given notes are approximations. Fiddlers ofter play this as a 'smear', filling a couple of beats with a version of a major scale played very fast, eg. measures 15, 220-221, 286 and 302-303. If played quickly enough most any descending scale will do.

"Sally Johnson" is played in the Texas manner between MM=112-120

The fourth measure of some of the sections sound best with a 'D' chord. For example check measures 44, 60, 85, 100, 108, 132, 220 and 228.

Herman Johnson (Photo by Brooks Otis)

SALLY JOHNSON

33
41
49
57
65

73
81
89
97
105

113
121
129
137
145

153
(2)
161
169
177
185

193
201
209
217
225

233
241
249
3
257
3
3
265

273
281
289
297

DUSTY MILLER

"Dusty Miller" is probably named after a traditional quilt pattern. It is a tune with a strong modal flavor, ie. sometimes it is neither major nor minor. The mix of 'g' naturals and 'g' sharps is the culprit.

Three variations of the basic melody start this arrangement. Often accompanists play only 'A' chords in this tune while others throw in an occasional 'G'. I detect three slightly different chord progressions, although they are a bit arbitrary. The second starts at measure 25 and the third at measure 49. Starting at measure 65 the different sections come and go. Just follow the chord progressions.

Benny Thomasson, Bartow Riley and Byron Berline are the sources for this rendition. Riley is a successful contest participant from Olton, Texas. Byron Berline, who was raised in Oklahoma won at Weiser in 1965 and '70. When he played with Bill Monroe and the Bluegrass Boys in 1967 he still played in Texas style. His contribution to this arrangement comes from those days. With a bluegrass band he had to play faster (MM=144), so there are more bowing slurs than usual between measures 57 and 65. Usually it is played around MM=112.

Thanks to Earl Spielman for the use of his transcriptions of this tune.

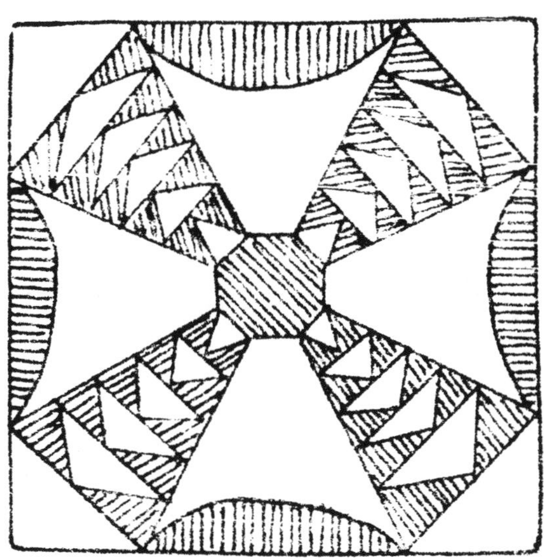

Dusty Miller quilt pattern.

DUSTY MILLER

33
41
49
G
A
E7
A
G
A
E7
A
57
65
G
A
G
A

73
E7
A
81
6
89
G
A
G
A
97
G
A
E7
A
G
A
E7
A
105

SALLY GOODIN

"Sally Goodin" is the prime example of Benny Thomasson's reference to tunes in the key of 'A' with "lots of volume, color and moves to them." Much of the volume is the result of the extensive use of 'a' and 'e' drones. Where they start and stop is a subjective decision. Just the right amount can be hypnotizing but not boring. I have frequently separated the staffs of the drone and melody notes in the music notation.

This version is based on the playing of Major Franklin, Benny Thomasson, Howdy Forrester, Vernon Solomon, J.T. Perkins and Eck Robertson. In 1922, having attended a Civil War veterans' reunion in Virginia, Alexander 'Eck' Robertson travelled to New York City in full rebel regalia and convinced RCA Victor to record him. This was probably the first recording of authentic country music. The resultant "Sally Goodin" had fourteen variations, one for every child of a mythical fiddler and his wife, Sally. There is some dispute as to how much of Robertson's version is owed to another Texas great, Lefty Franklin.

The first section, centering around 'c♯', makes obvious appearances at measures 1, 29, 73, 109, 121, 145, and 165. The next to last one features heavy metal fiddle - triple stops. Some fiddlers flatten the curvature of their bridge to facilitate this and double stops in general. Without flattening you can acheive something like a triple stop by exerting maximum bow pressure and playing near the neck.

The second sections are marked by a stress on 'e' notes. They begin at measures 9, 37, 78, and 157.

There are numerous third position variations of both parts throughout this rendition.

To break up the same continuous chord progression there is an 'F♯m' strain at measure 113. Then it is back to the usual Texas hoedown chords.

I have heard this played between MM=110 and 120.

SALLY GOODIN

73
81
⑷ ⑼
89
97

105
113
F♯m
A
F♯m
A
F♯m
A
121
129

137
145
153
161
169

DURANG'S HORNPIPE

"Durang's Hornpipe" was written in 1785 by a German dwarf named Hoffmeister. He named it for the first famous American dancer, hornpipe specialist, John Durang. It finally reached Texas and the result follows. Most of the hornpipe characteristics have disappeared, and it has developed into a two part tune with the second part featuring a modified descending bass line in its first four measures. As usual, by the end of the tune, the difference between sections starts breaking down.

Benny Thomasson, Major Franklin, J.T. Perkins and Dick Barret are the main contributors to this arrangement, played between MM=106 and 112.

Parade at Weiser Contest (Photo by Brooks Otis)

DURANG'S HORNPIPE

33
41
49
57
65

73
81
89
97
(1)
105

113
121
129
137
145
(1)
(0)
1.
2.
3

WALTZES

Waltzes are the black sheep of the fiddle world. They do not impress the general, unilluminated audience and use few fancy licks. Tone and control count most in this category. Some fiddlers feel guilty if they enjoy playing waltzes.

The problem is, many players learn these tunes divorced from the dances that are their foundations. All fiddlers should know something about square dancing, clogging, buck and wing, as well as waltzing. Search out a dance with a top caller and participate. After a few squares ask for a waltz and do it with your favorite partner. Then you will like waltzes.

Some of the characteristics of Texas waltzes are double-stopped slides, lots of long bow and, compared to hoedowns and tunes of choice, plenty of chords. They are usually done quite slowly. The quick waltzes I have included may be of Canadian origin, but they are popular with Texans.

KELLY'S WALTZ

Our first three step is typical of the genre, played slowly with lots of embellishments. This arrangement comes from the playing of Dick Barret and Benny Thomasson, the latter learning some of it from Hugh Farr of the Sons of the Pioneers.

The tune has four parts, the first contained in the first 32 measures with variations from measures 65-96 and 129 to the end. Compare the 'F♯7' with the 'Em' in the second measures, the 'C♯°' in measure 26 with its absence in the corresponding measures 90 and 154, and the 'Am' of measure 29 with the 'A7' of measures 93 and 157.

The second section begins at measures 33 and 97. Measure 108 adds an 'A7' chord which measure 44 passes up.

There is one setting for each of the third and fourth parts starting with measures 49 and 113, respectively.

Be careful that your slides are not too slow or the tune will sound too greasy. Hold the first notes as long as possible. The slide's time duration should be like a grace note.

The versions of this tune that I am familiar with are played around MM=116-120.

KELLY'S WALTZ

G
D7
G
57
C
G
D7
G
G
Em
67
G
C
G
Em
G
A7
78
D7
G
Em
G
C
G
88
C
G
E7
A7
D7
G
99
C
D7
G
D7

G C A7 D7
111 G C G
D7 G C
123 G D7 G
G Em G C
135 G G Em G
A7 D G
146 Em G C
G C G
156 E7 A7 D7 G

FIFTY YEARS AGO WALTZ

"Fifty Years Ago Waltz" alias "Blue Valley Waltz" is a plaintive one part tune with a hook in the 9th to 12th measures of each variation. I have given two possible chord progressions which, except for the 'F#7' in measure 54, are interchangeable. Mix and match to your heart's content.

The slides in measures 10, 26, 42, and 58 can be languid, but all others should be played crisply as mentioned in the introduction to "Kelly's Waltz".

The last variation ends with a nice string of double stops, ending with a typical Texas waltz coda, a 6th chord (here a 'b' over an 'f#'). This rendition is based on the playing of Mark O' Connor, Junior Dougherty and Bill Mitchell. The latter is from Tupelo, Mississippi and won the Tennessee Valley Fiddlers' Convention in 1967 and '68, and runner-up at Weiser in 1965 and '66.

I have heard the tune played between MM=108 and 124.

Bill Mitchell (Photo by Brooks Otis)

FIFTY YEARS AGO WALTZ

D
50
F♯m
Bm
D
F♯7
G
Gm
D
60
B7
E7
A7
D
A7
71
82
92

FORTY YEARS AGO WALTZ

As we look back into the more recent past we come up with a relative rarity in the contest world, a 'B♭' tune. Of course it is a slow one but the comparitive difficulty of this key causes some fiddlers to slack off to the key of 'A'. This rendition is based on the fiddling of J.T. Perkins and Benny Thomasson.

Remember to play the indicated eighth notes with a decided swing (3 ♩ ♪) to give the tune some bounce.

This is a two part arrangement, the first from measure 1-32, and the second from measure 33-64. Then a variation of each follows.

I have heard this played between MM=94-122, which is a pretty wide range. I prefer it on the fast side to minimize the pathetic nature of the melody.

FORTY YEARS AGO WALTZ

33
Gm
B♭
Gm
B♭
Gm
F7
42
B♭
Gm
B♭
52
Gm
B♭
E♭
E°
B♭
G7
C7
62
F7
72

82
92
102
114
124

MARTIN'S WALTZ

"Martin's Waltz" is mostly drawn from the playing of Benny Thomasson and Oklahoman J.C. Broughton and is usually done at about MM=108. It is another two part waltz that changes keys.

There is an alternate second section appended. End the tune by repeating the first section to the coda symbol and then skip to the final two measures.

Benny Thomasson (Photo by Brooks Otis)

MARTIN'S WALTZ

OOKPIK WALTZ

What a great name. It sounds a bit Eskimo. Well, why not? It is a real pretty melody with a minor feel. It is sometimes done in the key of 'G'.

This version is mostly based on the playing of Ace Sewell, an Oklahoman. I have heard it played between MM=120 and 140. As in "Martin's Waltz" repeat the first part until the coda sign to end it.

GOODNIGHT WALTZ

"Goodnight Waltz" is basically a one part tune, with that part played in two keys, 'C' and 'F'. There are a couple of harmonic vagaries which are voluntary. In measure 15 an 'A°' is used to delay returning to the tonic chord, 'C'. In the 'F' section the tune returns directly to the 'F' in its 15th measure (measure 47). In measure 29 a 'Dm' chord is used, while the corresponding measure in the 'F' section (measure 51) uses a 'G7'.

This interpretation is based on the playing of Mark O'Connor and the somewhat legendary Georgia Slim Rutland. The latter was a Southeasterner who played in Texas in the 1940's.

I have heard this waltz at about MM=126.

GOODNIGHT WALTZ

GERMAN WALTZ

"German Waltz" is a current favorite with Texans, with a bit of sound from the old Fatherland. The second sections (measures 11 and 45) summon echoes of courtly minuets. The seasoning of slurs and dotted eighth notes, while not arbitrary are, suggestions. Other wise this is a straight-foward arrangement.

Variations of the first section reappear at measures 29 and 54. A third section starts at measure twenty. Take the embellishing sixteenth note runs slowly until you get the feel.

This setting is based on playing by Dale Morris and Mark O'Connor. The former is from Decatur, Texas and won the Crockett Championship in 1979. The tempos I have heard vary wildly, from MM=112-140.

GERMAN WALTZ

33
D
A7
41
D
A7
D
A7
48
D
A7
D
A7
1.
D
2.
D
56
A7
D
1.
2.
D

FIDDLER'S WALTZ

Here is a real interesting arrangement of "Fiddler's Waltz". Each of the five sections has a little different chord progression. One notable aspect is that it slows down at the fifth section (measure 61) from about MM=150 to about MM=130. I do not know how all judges react to this kind of maneuver so you might want to split the difference and play it around MM=135.

Watch the staccato symbols in the first and third parts. They give this tune a touch of Vienna. The fourth part (measure 45) is also atypical of the Texas waltz with a long stream of fast notes. Play them with a light bow touch.

The fifth section is a gold mine of double stops. It is very demanding with frequent shifts to second and third position. The series of moves in measures 74 and 75 and measures 86 and 87 are especially blissful.

It is nice to pluck the last two notes, but watch it at contests. Anyway, this one is really worth going after. It is mostly based on Howdy Forrester's fiddling.

FIDDLER'S WALTZ

42
2.
G
D7
G
52
D7
G
62
D7
72
G
82
C
G
D7
G

MERRY WIDOW WALTZ

This one is so unadorned, it is almost naked. Take some of the embellishment ideas from the previous waltzes and dress it up. It is a quick waltz played around MM=165 and it sounds a bit Canadian to me. Texans occasionally show a liking to tunes from the Great White North.

The second section, based on Texas Shorty's playing, is the first one an octave higher. A typical fiddler's artifice.

I am sure that there is an older name for this tune but I have not been able to unearth it.

DANCE OF THE GOLDENROD

Finally a waltz without the word "waltz" in the title. This arrangement also cries out for festoons and garlands. My comments on "Merry Widow Waltz" also hold for this tune.

TUNES OF CHOICE

Rags and polkas appear to be the current favorites in this category with the former sometimes getting pretty swingy. Some contests have an open section that allows pretty much anything so I have included some double shuffle hokum to give you some ammunition. Remember, keep this stuff to a minimum. If you do it too much it becomes obvious that it is a lot easier to do than it sounds.

Some of the earmarks of this division are sixteen measure sections as opposed to the usual eight measures of hoedowns. There also are VI7 (E7 in the key of G) and II7 (A7 in the key of G) chords in these tunes. Their presence is enough for a tune to be classified a rag.

J. T. Perkins (Photo courtesy of The Devils Box)

RIVER ROAD

"River Road" is a very bouncy number done at about MM=102. It brought down the house at Weiser when Benny Thomasson played it in 1973. There are lots of double stops with sixths in them (eg. measures 1 and 38) giving this rendition a decidedly swing flavor. The 'D' chords can also be played as 'D6's.

It is a two section tune, with the second beginning at measure 17. A variation of the first section starts at measure 28. The last measure demonstrates the typical Texas bland fiddle ending lick, a little noodle down to the low tonic note.

RIVER ROAD

HOTFOOT

Here you can see that it is the chord progression that takes "Hotfoot" out of the hoedown domain. The playing is much the same as in Texas breakdowns though extended notes are more frequent here. This performance, taken from the playing of Benny Thomasson and Albert 'Red' Steeley (an old time fiddler from Fort Worth) is usually played between MM=112-118.

A couple of tunes by Steeley can be heard on "Texas Farewell" (County Records 517). A one time winner of the Dallas contest, he is a member of Hallettsville's Texas Fiddlers' Hall of Fame with such as Benny Thomasson, Major Franklin and Ervin Solomon.

HOTFOOT

TEXAS SCHOTTISCHE

The schottische is a Scots-derived round dance that has persisted in parts of the Northeast and Southwest of the United States. I have heard this one played at about MM=80 by Benny Thomasson, Texas Shorty and Junior Dougherty. This version has three parts. The first two are presented twice in the first 33 measures. After a third variation of the first part there is a four measure interlude at measure 43.

The final repetition of the first part has a no-no at straight contests, pizzicato. However, someday you may have a chance to play it for a caravan of Schottischers who will appreciate this correct touch.

In the 10th measure the time for the three note grace figure is taken from the preceeding 'e' note.

Start the 30th measure in third position to accomplish the slide from 'a' to the 'f#'.

TEXAS SCHOTTISCHE

26
A
E7
A
E7
A
34
D
A7
D
A7
41
1.
D
2.
D
E7
A
E7
A
E7
A
E7
A7
Play the first section once, then continue
47
pizz.
A
arco.
E7
pizz.
A
arco.
E7
A
Play the first section once to complete the tune

ALLENTOWN POLKA

Polkas are making a comeback with fiddlers. One play-through of ''Allentown Polka" will show how effective they can be on a fiddle. This is a real workout for your bowing hand with lots of string switching in the first section. Play it at about MM=120. It is a two part tune with the last four measures of each repeated to featherbed its length.

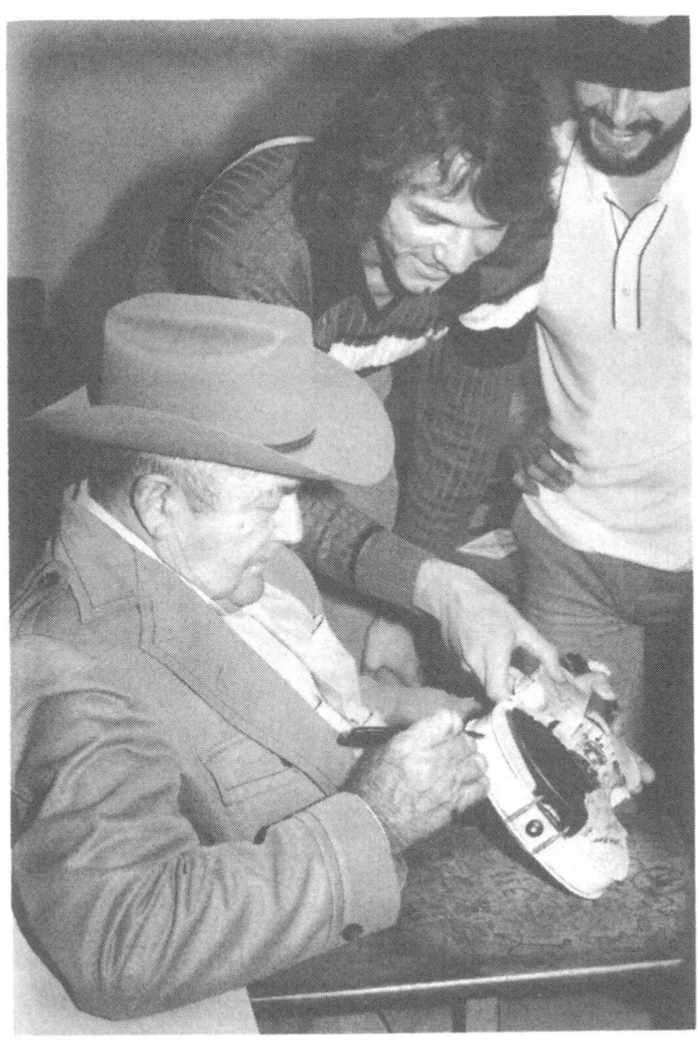

Major Franklin signing Mark O'Connor's fiddle at Dick Barrett's Invitational Fiddle Contest—Durant, OK; November 1978. (Photo by Marty O'Connor)

ALLENTOWN POLKA

JESSE POLKA

This is probably the most played contest polka though its length causes some of its five sections to be omitted. The historical connections between Texas and Mexico have also been musical, and a fiddler with a Mexican band tells me that "Jesse Polka" is derived from a tune called "Jesusito y Chihuahua". It is possible.

This conglomeration is based on fiddling by Texas Shorty, Mark O'Connor, Benny Thomasson and Loretta Brank. (See Mark O'Connor interview.) They play it between 104 and 116 MM.

It starts with two variations of the main section, switches to the key of 'C' in measure 33 for the second part and back to 'G' in measure 49 for the third. In the first and third parts the placement of the 'Am' and 'D7' chords can be altered to taste. A 'D7' could replace the minor.

A second strain of the first section begins at measure 64, and the fourth part, in the key of 'D' appears in measure 81. A variation of the third part begins at measure 97, followed by a variation of the second strain of the first section at measure 108. (Did that make sense? If not, just play it.) The second section appears again in measure 124 and a fifth part debuts in measure 140. This arrangement ends with a final first section variation.

The grace notes here borrow time from the previous notes, opposite to the usual order of things.

Try playing some swells (gentle crescendos) on the extended notes in the first section.

A simplified version of the first section is often plucked instead of bowed. Make the triplets and eighth notes of the first sixteen measures into quarter notes by leaving out some notes. This makes the pizzicato much easier.

JESSE POLKA

49
G
D7
G
Am
D7
G
58
D7
G
Am
D7
G
67
Am
D7
G
75
Am
A#°
G
Am
D7
G
D
A7
84
D
A7
D
A7

92
D
A7
D
G
D7
100
G
1.
Am
D7
G
2.
Am
D7
G
108
Am
D7
G
116
Am
A♯°
G
Am
D7
G
124
C
F
G
C

133
F
G7
C
C
142
G7
154
C
F
F#○
166
C
A7
D7
G7
C
C#
D7
G
Am
D7
178
G
Am
A#○
G
Am
D7
G

CALGARY POLKA

Here is a Canadian polka also known as "Gaudette Polka", based on Mark O'Connor's playing at about MM=118. It is a real bow burner when played at that tempo. Follow the bowing notation to get the right feel.

This is a three part tune with the first repeated for an ending. All 'D' chords may be played as 'Bm'.

F♯m
A
E7
D
A
Bm
E7
A
D
A
Bm
E7
A
F♯m
A
E7
A
F♯m
A
D
A
Bm
E7
A
D.S. al Coda
Coda
A

BEAUMONT RAG

This arrangement of "Beaumont Rag" contains all the elements of a Texan's idea of a rag with parts derived from Vernon Solomon, Benny Thomasson, Bob Wills and Johnny Gimble. In his younger days the latter was active in contests but his scintillating yet effortless stylings have earned him a life of ease in Nashville studios.

Occasionally four measures are left out to make the sections twelve measures long. As an example I have done that with the section that starts on measure 81. It can be done with any of the parts by omitting their ninth through twelfth measures. This ploy is connected with Bob Wills whose fiddling creativity is underrated by many.

The basic melody starts off the tune and is varied beginning at measures 48, 93 and 141. Of note is the diminised arpeggio of measure 61 and the tricky double stop arrangement starting at measure 93.

Different strains of a standard variation appear in measures 17, 65, 109 and 157. The high strain examples begin at measures 81 and 125. They require fourth position playing. (The index finger bars a 'c' over an 'f' on the top two strings.)

The final, rascal of variations features a double shuffle, which is usually prohibited at contests, but not always. The first strain enters at measure 33 and is not a full double shuffle. The full treatment uses all double stops. However it does exhibit the basic characteristic of repeated three note riffs, giving this part a continuous series of syncopations. Watch the bowing change in measure 42. A chic series of shuffles is introduced in measure 173. Measures 177-180 contain a truly classic modification of hokum to give a different sound.

"Beaumont Rag" is usually played close to MM=118.

Vernon Solomon at the Grand Ol' Opry (Photo by Brooks Otis)

BEAUMONT RAG

33
41
49
57
65
3

73
81
89
97
105

113
121
129
137
145

153
161
169
177
185

DON'T LET YOUR DEAL GO DOWN

"Don't Let Your Deal Go Down" is an old time tune that has been worked up into a Texas style rag. Like "Beaumont Rag" there is a basic melody around which a few standard variations have grown, one of which is the inevitable garish hokum. This tune was a favorite with fiddle oriented Western swing bands of the 1930's.

It starts out in the classic archaic style, with two 9 measure statements of the melody. An extra measure of 'E7' is added to create the slightly skewed old timey effect. All other sections have eight measures. You can omit the third measure of each 'E7' to square up the tune. You can also occasionally add one. Your accompanists will appreciate that. Other variations of this part begin at measures 51, 59, 131, 139, 183, and 231. An offshoot of this section starts at measures 115 and 123, where 'C' chords replace 'A7's.

The high strains begin on measures 19, 27 (actually a low variety of the high strain) 67, 75, 147, 192, and 200. The slides in sections can be stretched out. Stressing them thusly gives the tune an uninhibited sound. The trick is to slide leisurely but not sloppily. In measures 193 and 201 the 'd' in parentheses is about where the slide ends.

Check out measures 204-207. They contain a fine improvised riff by Mark O'Connor taken from an exhibition round at Weiser. He played it at about MM=138, a bit too risky for contest rounds. Try doing the whole tune at that tempo. Wow! Otherwise I have usually heard it between MM=112 and 120.

The rest of the sections contain motifs that first gently border upon (measures 35 through 50) and then joyfully enter the Land of Hokum. This excursion climaxes with some unabashed fiddle humbuggery in measures 208-232. I confess that I may be a bit hard on the double shuffle. This attitude stems from the misuse of it by some and the overkill of "Orange Blossom Special". The usual shuffle of "O.B.S." is actually quite easy. The riff starting in the 216th measure is much more demanding and interesting.

The anticipation of the 'E7' chord in measure 90, with an 'A♭' note played over a 'G' chord, works because, by this time, the listener's ear is acclimated to expect the notes in an 'E7' scale on the next downbeat.

Do not let all the slide symbols in measures 175-178 daunt you. Take it slowly. You should then recognize the syncopation pattern.

Johnny Gimble, Vernon Solomon, Mark O'Connor, Benny Thomasson, J.C. Broughton and Louis Franklin all contributed to this arrangement. The latter is from Whitewright, Texas and has won many contests including the World Championship seven times.

J. C. Broughton (Photo by Brooks Otis)

DON'T LET YOUR DEAL GO DOWN

75
83
91
99
107

115
E7
C
D7
G
125
E7
A7
135
D7
G
143
151
1.
2.

159
167
175
182
1.
2.
192

200
208
216
224
232

TWINKLE LITTLE STAR

Here is a neat tune that does not quite fit into any category, so it is played as a tune of choice. It is a two section arrangement with a variation on each part included. I have taken the ideas from J.T. Perkins and Benny Thomasson who play it between MM=114 and 118.

Em
Am
D7
G
33
C
G
Em
A7
D7
41
G
C
G
Em
Am
D7
G
49
D7
G
59
C
G
Em
Am
D7
G

SAY OLD MAN

"Say old man can you play the fiddle,

Yes sir, I can fiddle just a little."

So sang Eck Robertson when he played "Say Old Man". This is another tune of unidentifiable species because its modal eccentricities are not usually expected in the hoedown category. Is it in major or minor? It cannot seem to make a decision so it drifts back and forth. Sometimes fiddlers play an Em scale in the first section but accompanists play E major. Some fiddlers sharp the 'c' in this section, confusing the issue even more. On the other hand measures 94-109 sound quite alright if the 'g' and 'c' are played as naturals and 'Em' chords are played over them.

Occasionally an 'A' chord is played in the major sections. Guitarists seem quite perplexed by this piece. Many fiddle tunes come from a time and place where there was no accompaniment, so the players did not worry about chord structure. This appears to be one of that type.

Three different strains of the first section begin things. The second section goes from measures 21-29 leading to a key change for the next two parts. The first 29 measures are sometimes played with a Major Franklin style bouncing bow.

In non-contest situations fiddlers often retune their 'g' string down to an 'e' on this number. Using it as a drone from measures 54-69 gives a haunting sound. The drone could also be used through most of measures 91-97.

Starting at the 70th measure are a series of strains of another E major section. The 'A' chords are optional as are the 'B7' chords in the first section.

This unique and beautiful tune and its variations are based on the playing of Howdy Forrester, Eck Robertson, Benny Thomasson, Mark O'Connor and Larry Franklin. The latter is the son of Louis Franklin (see "Don't Let Your Deal Go Down") and winner of the 1982 National Collegiate Contest at East Texas State University. (His father won this four times.) All the versions I have heard are played right at MM=112.

SAY OLD MAN

B7
E
42
Em
Am
Em
Am
Em
50
Em
B7
Em
58
B7
Em
66
E
(A)
E
74
(A)
1.
B7
E

2.
B7
E
82
1.
2.
90
98
106
114

FIDDLE ASSOCIATIONS

This list was compiled from The Devil's Box magazine.

1. Tennessee Valley Old Time Fiddlers' Association
   305 Stella Drive
   Madison, Alabama 35758
2. Arizona Old Time Fiddlers' Association
   c/o Shoup
   4717 East Mulberry Street
   Phoenix, Arizona 85018
3. National Old Time Fiddlers' Association
   c/o Wilson
   P.O. Box 265
   Dragoon, Arizona 85609
4. Southern Arizona O.T.F.A.
   P.O. Box 5334
   Tucson, Arizona 85717
5. California State O.T.F.A.
   P.O. Box 1703
   Oroville, California 95969
6. Central California O.T.F.A.
   c/o Davis
   2805 Charlotte Avenue
   Ceres, California 95307
7. Santa Clara Valley F.A.
   P.O. Box 18462
   San Jose, California 95158
8. Southern California O.T.F.A.
   c/o Moore
   Star Route, Box 89
   Caliente, California 93518
9. Florida State F.A.
   1645 S.W. Rocky Point Road
   Gainesville, Florida 32608

10. Idaho O.T.F.A.
c/o Signal - American
Box 709
Weiser, Idaho 83672

11. Illinois O.T.F.A.
211 West South Fourth Street
Shelbyville, Illinois 62565

12. Southern Indiana F.A.
c/o Nicholson
Route 3
Salem, Indiana 47167

13. Michigan F.A.
c/o White
4245 Okemos Road
Okemos, Michigan 48864

14. Original Michigan F.A.
c/o Bettesworth
G-5035 Flushing Road
Flushing, Michigan 48433

15. Missouri Fiddlers' and Country Music Association
9245 Whitecliff Park Lane
Crestwood, Missouri 63126

16. Montana State Fiddlers' Organization
c/o Stark
3901 Becraft Lane
Billings, Montana 59101

17. Nevada O.T.F.A.
c/o Germain
7969 Rodeo Road
Las Vegas, Nevada 89119

18. New York O.T.F.A.

c/o Clemens

R.D. 1

Redfield, New York 13437

19. Oklahoma State F.A.

c/o Thede

1824 N.W. 23rd Street

Oklahoma City, Oklahoma 73106

20. Oregon O.T.F.A.

c/o Tucker

8349 Booth Road

Klamath Falls, Oregon 97601

21. Old Time Fiddlers of Southwest Pennsylvania

Box 457

McClellardtown, Pennsylvania 15458

22. Texas O.T.F.A.

P.O. Box 132

Gustine, Texas 76455

23. Northeast F.A.

191 Woodlawn Road

Burlington, Vermont 05401

SOME FIDDLE CONTESTS

Here is a selected list of fiddle contests of all sizes, current as of 1982. I have picked ones that have some longevity and thus show signs of continuing for many years. Believe me, this inventory, though representative, is a drop in the big bucket of fiddle conventions. Writing to the Town Hall or Chamber of Commerce of the indicated towns will probably elicit dates and exact locations of these affairs.

1. Cahaba Shrine Temple Fiddling & Bluegrass Convention
   Huntsville, Alabama
2. State Championship Old Time Fiddlers' Contest
   Payson, Arizona
3. SPBGMA Annual Fiddle Championship
   Mountain View, Arkansas
4. Old Time Fiddlers' Contest
   Torrance, California
5. Northwest Georgia Fiddlers' Championships
   Davis Farm
   Chickamauga, Georgia
6. National Old Time Fiddle Contest
   Weiser, Idaho
7. Gatherin' at the Mounds Fiddlers' Convention
   Dickson Mounds, Illinois
8. Annual National Country Music Contest
   Avoca, Iowa
9. Annual Fiddlers' and Traditional Musicians' Gathering
   Battleground, Iowa
10. Mid-America Old Time Music Contest and Exposition
    Council Bluffs, Iowa

11. Kentucky Fiddlers' Contest and Convention
    Route 5, Box 449
    Elizabethtown, Kentucky
12. Annual Kentucky State Fiddlers' Championship
    Rough River State Park
    Falls of Rough, Kentucky
13. Annual Ohio Valley Championship Fiddling Convention
    Town Square Mall
    Owensboro, Kentucky
14. East Benton Fiddle Convention
    East Benton, Maine
15. Michigan State Championship Old Time Fiddlers' Contest
    New Boston, Michigan
16. Minnesota State Championship Old Time Fiddle Contest
    Cotton, Minnesota
17. Missouri State Fiddling Championship
    Columbia, Missouri
18. Acres of Diamonds Old Time Fiddlers' Contest
    St. Joseph, Missouri
19. Crawford Fiddle Contest
    Crawford, Nebraska
20. Bluegrass and Old Time Fiddling Contest
    Silver City, New Mexico
21. Annual Fiddlers' Convention
    Mount Airy, North Carolina
22. Annual Fiddler's Grove Festival
    Union Grove, North Carolina
23. World Series of Fiddling
    Langley, Oklahoma

24. Tulsa State Fair Fiddle Contest

    State Fair Grounds

    Tulsa, Oklahoma

25. Wacamaw Riverfest Fiddlers' Convention

    Conway, South Carolina

26. South Dakota and Open Fiddling Contest

    Yankton, South Dakota

27. International Championship Old Time Fiddle Contest

    River Front Park

    Chattanooga, Tennessee

28. Tennessee State Fiddle Championships

    Clarksville, Tennessee

29. Memphis in May Fiddlers' Convention

    Memphis, Tennessee

30. Grand Masters' Fiddle Contest

    Opryland Park

    Nashville, Tennessee

31. Fiddlers' Jamboree

    Smithville, Tennessee

32. Bob Wills Memorial Fiddle Contest

    Amarillo, Texas

33. Annual National Collegiate Fiddlers' Festival

    East Texas State University

    Commerce, Texas

34. Annual East Texas Yamboree Fiddlers' Contest

    Gilmer, Texas

35. Texas State Fiddle Championships

    Knights of Columbus Hall

    Hallettsville, Texas

36. Annual Fiddlers' Convention

Longview, Texas

37. Red River Valley Exposition Fiddlers' Contest

Paris, Texas

38. Sinton Old Time Fiddle Festival

Sinton, Texas

39. Bluegrass Band and Fiddle Contest

Winnie, Texas

40. National Traditional Old Time Fiddlers' and Step Dancers' Contest

Barre, Vermont

41. Fiddle Contest

Craftsberry Common, Vermont

42. Annual Galax Old Time Fiddlers' Convention

Felts Park

Galax, Virginia

43. Annual Bluefield Old Time and Bluegrass Fiddlers' Convention

New Glenwood Park

Bluefield, West Virginia

44. Maritime Old Time Fiddling Contest

Prince Andrew High School

Dartmouth, Nova Scotia, Canada

45. Annual Fiddlers' Contest

Petrolia, Ontario, Canada

46. Canadian Open Old Time Fiddlers' Contest

Shelburne, Ontario, Canada

47. Western Canadian Amateur Old Time Fiddling Championships

Swift Current, Saskatchewan, Canada

BIBLIOGRAPHY

1. John Edwards Memorial Foundation Quarterly

   a) Eck Robertson Interview by Earl Spielman (Winter 1972)

   b) Benny Thomasson Interview by Michael Mendelson (Autumn 1974)

   c) The 1920 Georgia Old Time Fiddle Convention by Wayne W. Daniel (Summer 1980)

2. Traditional Music and Social Change: The Old Time Fiddlers' Association Movement in the United States by Richard Blaustein (Indiana University PhD thesis, 1975)

3. Traditional North American Fiddling: A Methodology by Earl Spielman (University of Wisconsin at Madison PhD thesis, 1975)

4. The Music of Black Americans by Eileen Southern (Norton and Co, 1971)

5. Tennessee Strings by Charles K. Wolfe (University of Tennessee Press, 1976)

6. Bluegrass Fiddle Styles by Stacy Phillips and Kenny Kosek (Oak Publications 1978)

7. The Devil's Box (305 Stella Drive, Madison, Alabama 35758)

   a) The First Annual Country Fiddle Contest by Richard Hulan (March 1969)

   b) Fiddling Eck Robertson by John Cohen (June 1972)

   c) The Great 1927 Nashville Fiddlers' Contest by Charles Wolfe (September 1973)

   d) Benny Thomasson Interview by David Garelick (March 1974)

   e) Howdy Forrester by Perry Harris and Howard Roberts (June 1974)

   f) Curly Fox by Ivan Tribe (December 1974)

   g) Bill Mitchell by Bill Harrison (December 1976)

   h) A Cowboy Fiddling Contest in the Dakotas by Richard Blaustein (December 1976)

   i) The Atlanta Fiddling Contests by Charles Wolfe (June 1980)

   j) An 1899 Fiddlers' Carnival by Charles Wolfe (December 1980)

   k) On Gypsies, Chancellors and Breakdowns by Bob Stoddard (March 1982)

   l) Bob Wills the Fiddler by Charles Wolfe (June 1982)

   m) Celebrating a Decade of Excellence by Bill Harrison (Sept. 1982)

   n) The 1982 Texas State Fiddlers' Contest by Bill Northcutt (September 1982)

8. The backs of some of the albums listed in the Discography contain pertinent information.

9. Texas Fiddle Style: An Exploratory Study by Mary Morrow (University of Texas - Austin undergraduate thesis, 1980)

10. An Analytical Methodology for the Study of Regional Fiddle Styles Applied to Texas Style Fiddling by Margaret Schultz (Eastern Washington University undergraduate thesis, 1977)

DISCOGRAPHY

The best place to hunt for these albums is to get in touch with County Sales, P.O. Box 191, Floyd, Virginia 24091.

1. County 410 - East Texas Seranaders 1927-1936 (recordings of a Texas fiddle band)
2. County 517 - Texas Farewell (several performers including Eck Robertson, Red Steeley, Ervin Solomon and Oscar Harper)
3. County 525 - Fiddlers' Convention, Mountain City, Tennessee (early recordings of Southeastern fiddlers who entered contests)
4. County 703 - Texas Hoedown (1965 recordings of Bartow Riley, Vernon Solomon and Benny Thomasson)
5. County 707 - Texas Fiddle Favorites (1966 recordings of Norman Solomon, Major Franklin and Lewis Franklin)
6. County 724 - Country Fiddling from the Big State (Benny Thomasson in 1970 with several pieces played in cross tunings)
7. Davis Unlimited 33007 - Just Fine Fiddling (J.T. Perkins)
8. Davis Unlimited 33017 - Fiddle Favorites (J.T. Perkins)
9. Davis Unlimited 33038 - Texas Breakdown (Vernon Solomon)
10. Rounder 046 - Mark O'Connor (recorded when he was about fifteen)
11. Rounder 100 - Dad's Favorites (Byron Berline's tribute to his father, an old time Texas fiddler)
12. Rounder 137 - Soppin' the Gravy (Mark O'Connor in 1979)
13. OMAC 1 - Texas Jam Session (some wild fiddling by Benny Thomasson, Texas Shorty, Mark O'Connor and Terry Morris)

14. OMAC 2 - In Concert (just a few fiddle numbers, with Mark O'Connor, Byron Berline and Sam Bush)
15. MGM E4035 - Fancy Fiddlin' Country Style (Howdy Forrester at his best, one day it will surely be re-released)
16. UA 3295 - Big Howdy Fiddlin' Country Style (as above)
17. Stoneway 127 - Howdy's Fiddle (Howdy Forrester in the 1970's)
18. Stoneway 136 - Big Howdy (as above)
19. Stoneway 150 - Leather Britches (as above)
20. Stoneway 168 - Stylish Fiddling (as above)
21. Voyager 309 - Jam Session with Benny and Jerry Thomasson (recorded at the Weiser campgrounds in 1972)
22. Sonyatone 201 - Eck Robertson Master Fiddler (all his early recordings)
23. Kanawha 315 - Panhandle Texas Fiddle (Bartow Riley)
24. Kanawha 601 - Twin Fiddling Country Style (radio transcriptions of Howdy Forrester and Slim Rutland)
25. Kanawha (number unknown) - Raw Fiddle (unaccompanied playing by Slim Rutland)
26. American Heritage 1 - Championship Fiddling (Herman Johnson)
27. American Heritage 515 - The 1974 Weiser Festival Top Five (there are a limited amount of these available for selected years)
28. CMH 9027 - The Texas Fiddle Album (Johnny Gimble)
29. Many consistent high finishers put out their own records which they sell at contests. Among these are Herman Johnson, Texas Shorty Chancellor, Dick Barret and Junior Dougherty.
30. Voyager 319 - S - Southwestern Fiddling (Ace Sewell)
31. Elektra 285 - The Dillards - Pickin' and Fiddlin' (The Dillards back up Byron Berline on an all Texas fiddle album. mid - 1960's)

OUTRODUCTION

If you have gone through this book diligently I am sure that you have a renewed sense of respect for fiddling. The next step is to get ready to play this music with others. Here are some suggestions.

1. Listen to some of the records listed in the Discography.
2. Try to locate a fiddle jam session in which to partake. (Timidly at first, until you are sure of yorself. Jam session etiquette is a whole other can of worms.)
3. Persuade the area square dance caller to employ a band, not a record player. Threats and strong-arm tactics should be used only as a last resort.
4. Get in touch with the nearest fiddle association (see listing elsewhere in this book) for some advice and contacts. Some sponsor jam sessions.
5. Go to some contests with your tape recorder in hand.
6. Practice a lot.

Here are some other tunes frequently played by Texas style fiddlers at contests.

Hoedowns	Waltzes	Tunes of Choice
Grey Eagle Hornpipe	Shannon	Lone Star Rag
Rocky Mountain Goat	Wednesday Night	Herman's Rag
Bill Cheatem	Lucinda	Florida Blues
Jack O'Diamonds	Sweet Bunch of Daisies	Red Apple Rag
Soppin' the Gravy	Festival	Side by Side Schottische
Fisher's Hornpipe	Westphalia	B and B Rag
Whiskey Before Breakfast	Roxanna	Clarinet Polka
Tugboat	Kentucky	Cotton Patch Rag
Miller's Reel	Gardenia	Dill Pickles
Londonderry Hornpipe	Chancellor's	Limerock

I welcome all comments and questions. See you at the next contest.

Made in United States
Orlando, FL
02 May 2022